THE VISUAL
DICTIONARY *of the*
SKELETON

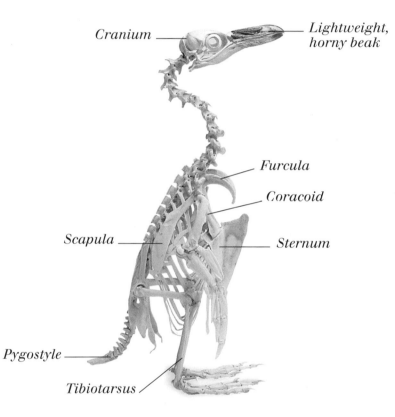

Cranium —

Lightweight,
horny beak

Furcula

Coracoid

Scapula —

Sternum

Pygostyle —

Tibiotarsus

PENGUIN SKELETON

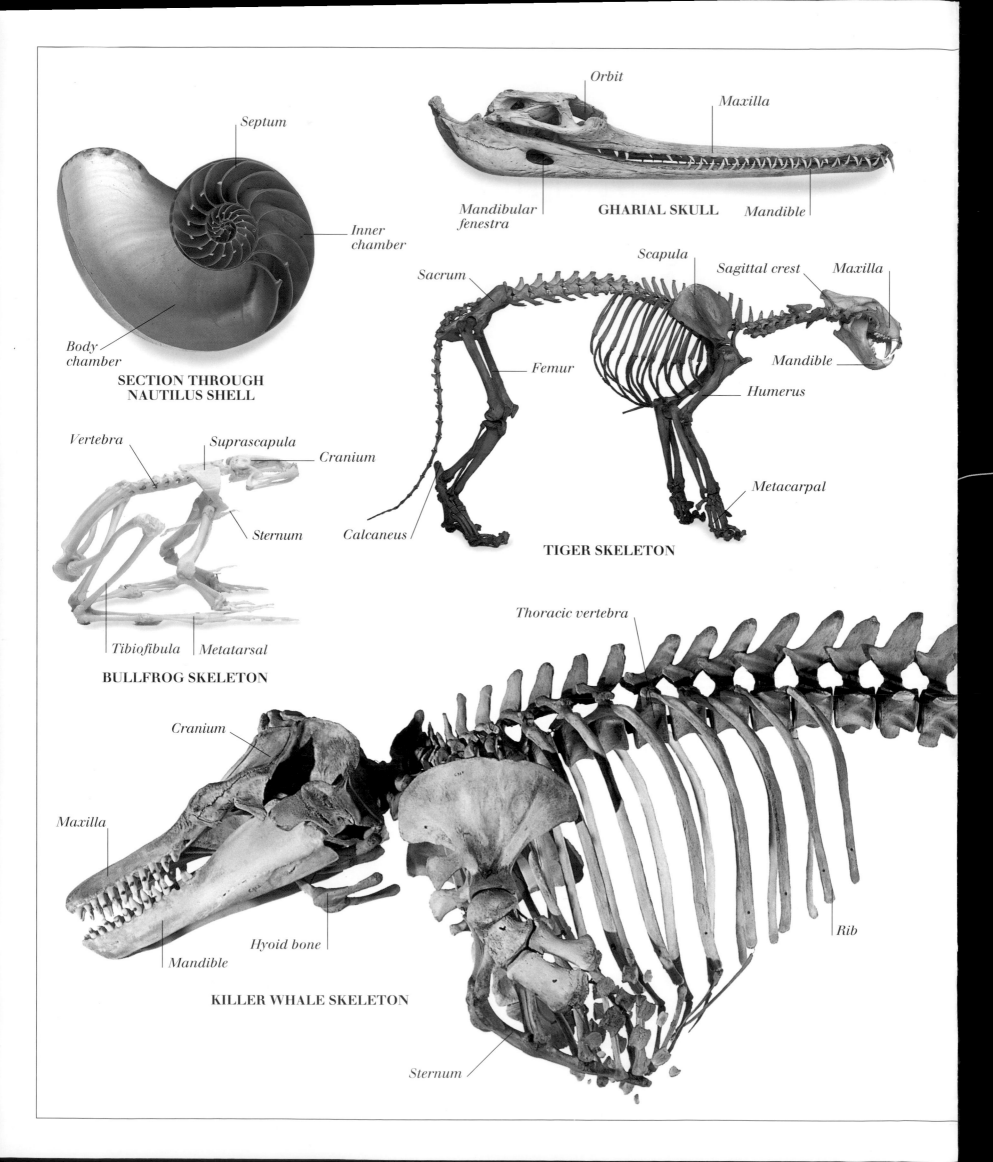

Septum

Inner chamber

Body chamber

SECTION THROUGH NAUTILUS SHELL

Orbit

Maxilla

Mandibular fenestra

GHARIAL SKULL

Mandible

Scapula

Sagittal crest

Maxilla

Sacrum

Femur

Mandible

Humerus

Calcaneus

Metacarpal

TIGER SKELETON

Vertebra

Suprascapula

Cranium

Sternum

Tibiofibula

Metatarsal

BULLFROG SKELETON

Thoracic vertebra

Cranium

Maxilla

Hyoid bone

Mandible

Rib

KILLER WHALE SKELETON

Sternum

THE VISUAL
DICTIONARY *of the*
SKELETON

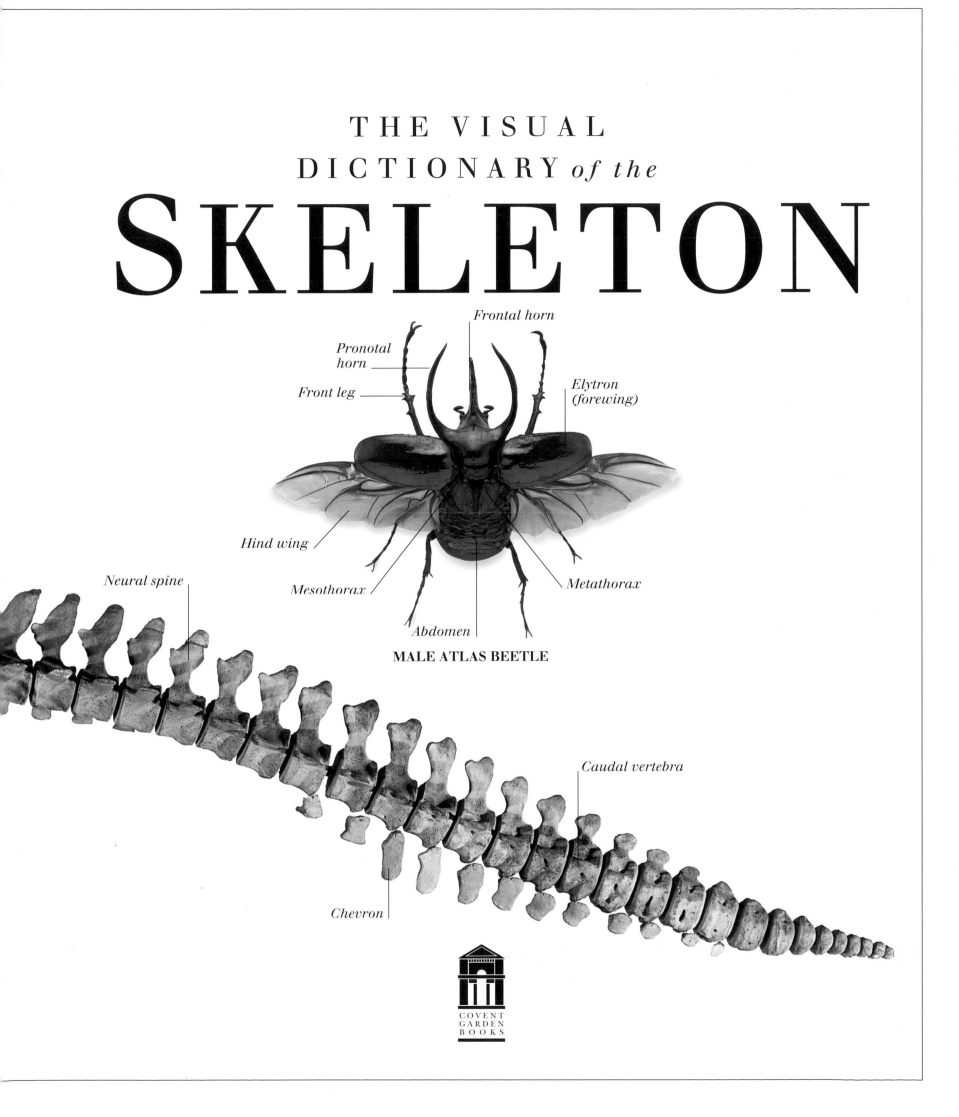

Frontal horn

Pronotal
horn

Front leg

Elytron
(forewing)

Hind wing

Neural spine

Mesothorax

Metathorax

Abdomen

MALE ATLAS BEETLE

Caudal vertebra

Chevron

COVENT
GARDEN
BOOKS

A DORLING KINDERSLEY BOOK

PROJECT ART EDITOR CHRIS WALKER
DESIGNER HELEN BENFIELD

PROJECT EDITOR FIONA COURTENAY-THOMPSON
EDITORIAL ASSISTANT WILL HODGKINSON
CONSULTANT EDITOR DR. RICHARD WALKER

MANAGING ART EDITOR BRYN WALLS
MANAGING EDITORS RUTH MIDGLEY, MARTYN PAGE

ILLUSTRATIONS JOANNA CAMERON, DEBORAH MAIZELS, GRAHAM ROSEWARNE, JOHN TEMPERTON

PICTURE RESEARCH INGRID NILSSON

PRODUCTION HILARY STEPHENS

This edition published in 1999 by Covent Garden Books

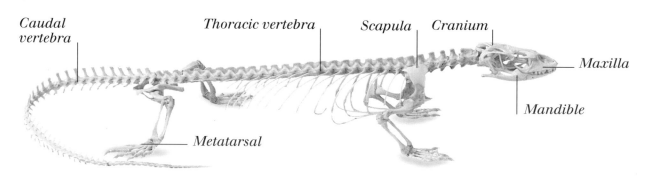

Caudal vertebra   *Thoracic vertebra*   *Scapula*   *Cranium*   *Maxilla*   *Mandible*   *Metatarsal*

MONITOR LIZARD SKELETON

FIRST PUBLISHED IN GREAT BRITAIN IN 1995
BY DORLING KINDERSLEY LIMITED
9 HENRIETTA STREET, LONDON WC2E 8PS
WWW.DK.COM
COPYRIGHT © 1995 DORLING KINDERSLEY LIMITED, LONDON

A CIP CATALOGUE RECORD FOR THIS BOOK IS AVAILABLE FROM THE BRITISH LIBRARY

ISBN 1-871-854-652

REPRODUCED BY COLOURSCAN, SINGAPORE
PRINTED AND BOUND BY ARTES GRÁFICAS TOLEDO, S.A.
D.L. TO: 609 - 1999

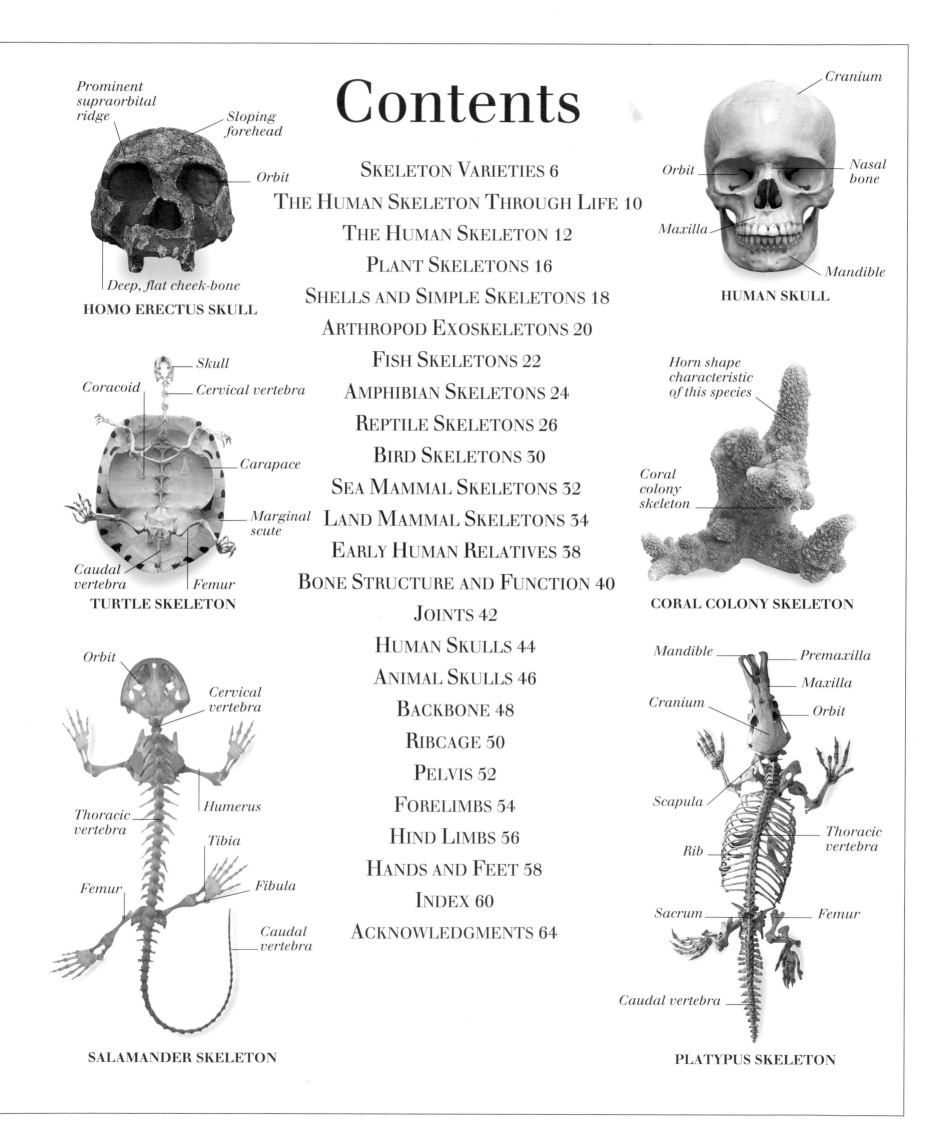

Contents

Prominent
supraorbital
ridge

Sloping
forehead

Orbit

Deep, flat cheek-bone

HOMO ERECTUS SKULL

Cranium

Orbit

Nasal
bone

Maxilla

Mandible

HUMAN SKULL

Skull

Coracoid

Cervical vertebra

Carapace

Marginal
scute

Caudal
vertebra

Femur

TURTLE SKELETON

Horn shape
characteristic
of this species

Coral
colony
skeleton

CORAL COLONY SKELETON

Orbit

Cervical
vertebra

Thoracic
vertebra

Humerus

Tibia

Femur

Fibula

Caudal
vertebra

SALAMANDER SKELETON

Mandible

Premaxilla

Maxilla

Cranium

Orbit

Scapula

Rib

Thoracic
vertebra

Sacrum

Femur

Caudal vertebra

PLATYPUS SKELETON

Skeleton varieties 1

THE SKELETON IS A SUPPORTIVE framework that maintains the shape of an organism and protects its internal organs. In many animals, the skeleton also plays a vital role in movement. There are two main types of skeleton: internal skeletons (endoskeletons) and external skeletons (exoskeletons). Vertebrates (animals with backbones) – fish, amphibians, reptiles, birds, and mammals – have endoskeletons, which are usually made of bone. A few vertebrates, such as boxfish and tortoises, have both endoskeletons and exoskeletons. Most invertebrates (animals without backbones) have exoskeletons. These include the body cases of insects and crustaceans, the shells of snails, and the tests of sea urchins. Some single-celled organisms also have exoskeletons; for example, the outer coat of diatoms. Other types of skeleton include the hydrostatic (fluid-filled) skeleton of earthworms, and plant skeletons, which consist of various elements, such as xylem, that help to support roots, stems, and leaves.

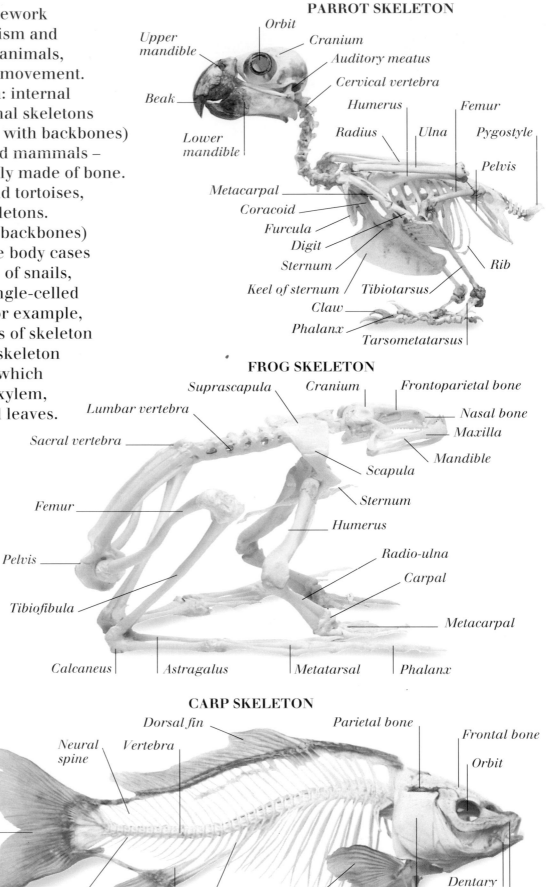

PARROT SKELETON

Orbit
Upper mandible
Cranium
Auditory meatus
Cervical vertebra
Beak
Humerus
Femur
Radius
Ulna
Pygostyle
Lower mandible
Pelvis
Metacarpal
Coracoid
Furcula
Digit
Sternum
Rib
Keel of sternum
Tibiotarsus
Claw
Phalanx
Tarsometatarsus

FROG SKELETON

Suprascapula
Cranium
Frontoparietal bone
Lumbar vertebra
Nasal bone
Sacral vertebra
Maxilla
Mandible
Scapula
Sternum
Femur
Humerus
Radio-ulna
Pelvis
Carpal
Tibiofibula
Metacarpal
Calcaneus
Astragalus
Metatarsal
Phalanx

LIZARD SKELETON

Metacarpal
Cranium
Phalanx
Orbit
Cervical vertebra
Carpal
Radius
Scapula
Ulna
Rib
Thoracolumbar vertebra
Sacrum
Femur
Pelvis
Tibia
Tarsal
Phalanx
Metatarsal
Caudal vertebra

CARP SKELETON

Dorsal fin
Parietal bone
Frontal bone
Neural spine
Vertebra
Orbit
Caudal fin
Dentary bone
Haemal spine
Rib
Pectoral fin
Maxilla
Anal fin
Interhaemal
Pelvic fin
Opercular bone

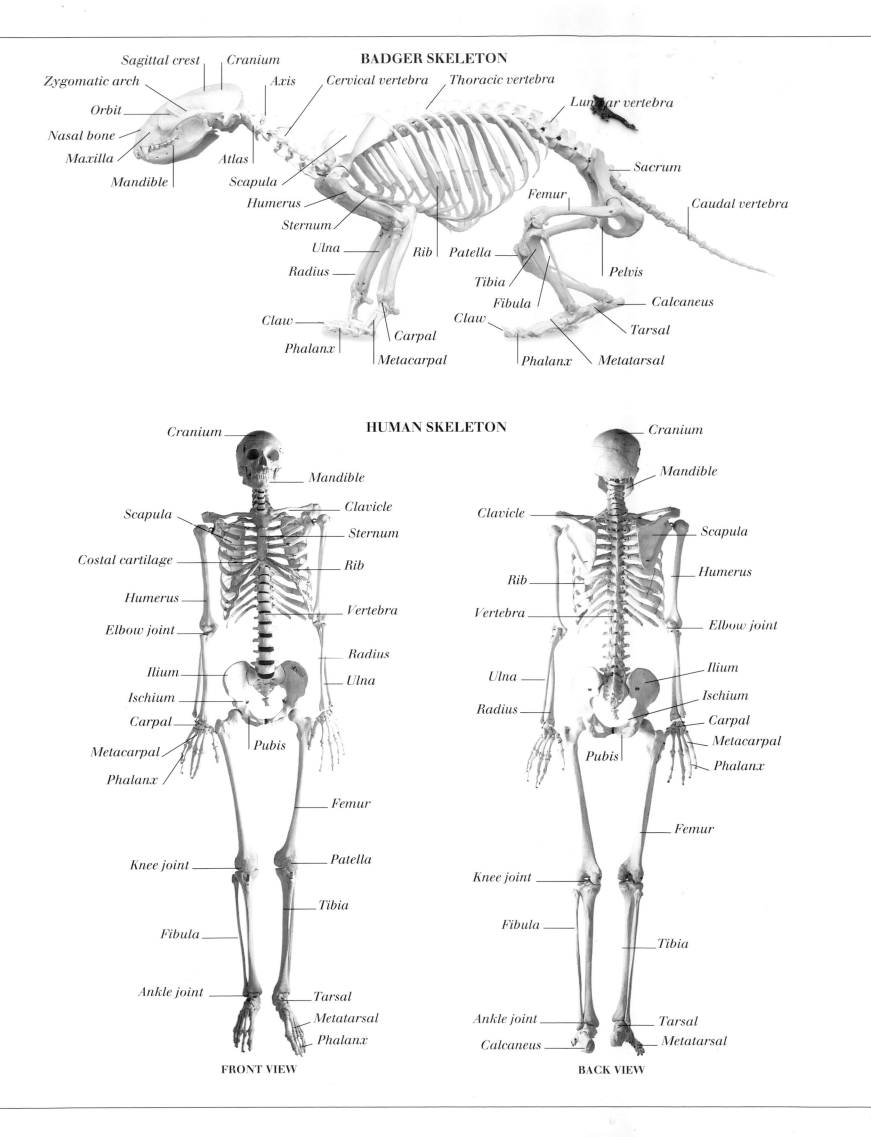

BADGER SKELETON

Sagittal crest
Cranium
Zygomatic arch
Axis
Cervical vertebra
Thoracic vertebra
Lumbar vertebra
Orbit
Nasal bone
Maxilla
Atlas
Mandible
Scapula
Humerus
Sternum
Sacrum
Caudal vertebra
Ulna
Rib
Patella
Femur
Radius
Tibia
Pelvis
Fibula
Calcaneus
Claw
Claw
Tarsal
Phalanx
Carpal
Phalanx
Metatarsal
Metacarpal

HUMAN SKELETON

Cranium
Cranium
Mandible
Mandible
Scapula
Clavicle
Clavicle
Sternum
Scapula
Costal cartilage
Rib
Rib
Humerus
Humerus
Vertebra
Vertebra
Elbow joint
Elbow joint
Radius
Ilium
Ilium
Ulna
Ischium
Ischium
Carpal
Ulna
Carpal
Metacarpal
Radius
Metacarpal
Pubis
Phalanx
Pubis
Phalanx
Femur
Femur
Knee joint
Patella
Tibia
Knee joint
Fibula
Fibula
Tibia
Ankle joint
Tarsal
Ankle joint
Tarsal
Metatarsal
Calcaneus
Metatarsal
Phalanx

FRONT VIEW

BACK VIEW

Skeleton varieties 2

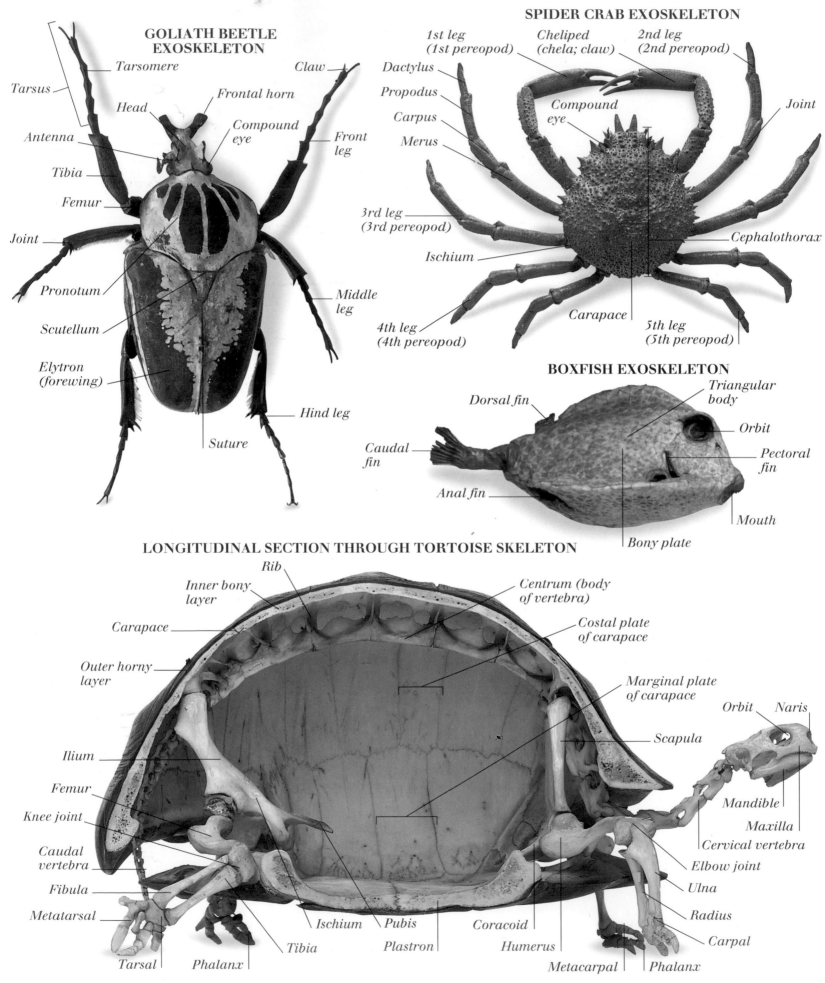

GOLIATH BEETLE EXOSKELETON

Tarsus
Tarsomere
Head
Antenna
Tibia
Femur
Joint
Pronotum
Scutellum
Elytron (forewing)
Claw
Frontal horn
Compound eye
Front leg
Middle leg
Hind leg
Suture

SPIDER CRAB EXOSKELETON

1st leg (1st pereopod)
Dactylus
Propodus
Carpus
Merus
3rd leg (3rd pereopod)
Ischium
4th leg (4th pereopod)
Cheliped (chela; claw)
Compound eye
2nd leg (2nd pereopod)
Joint
Cephalothorax
Carapace
5th leg (5th pereopod)

BOXFISH EXOSKELETON

Dorsal fin
Caudal fin
Anal fin
Triangular body
Orbit
Pectoral fin
Mouth
Bony plate

LONGITUDINAL SECTION THROUGH TORTOISE SKELETON

Rib
Inner bony layer
Carapace
Outer horny layer
Ilium
Femur
Knee joint
Caudal vertebra
Fibula
Metatarsal
Tarsal
Phalanx
Tibia
Ischium
Pubis
Plastron
Coracoid
Humerus
Centrum (body of vertebra)
Costal plate of carapace
Marginal plate of carapace
Orbit
Naris
Scapula
Mandible
Maxilla
Cervical vertebra
Elbow joint
Ulna
Radius
Carpal
Metacarpal
Phalanx

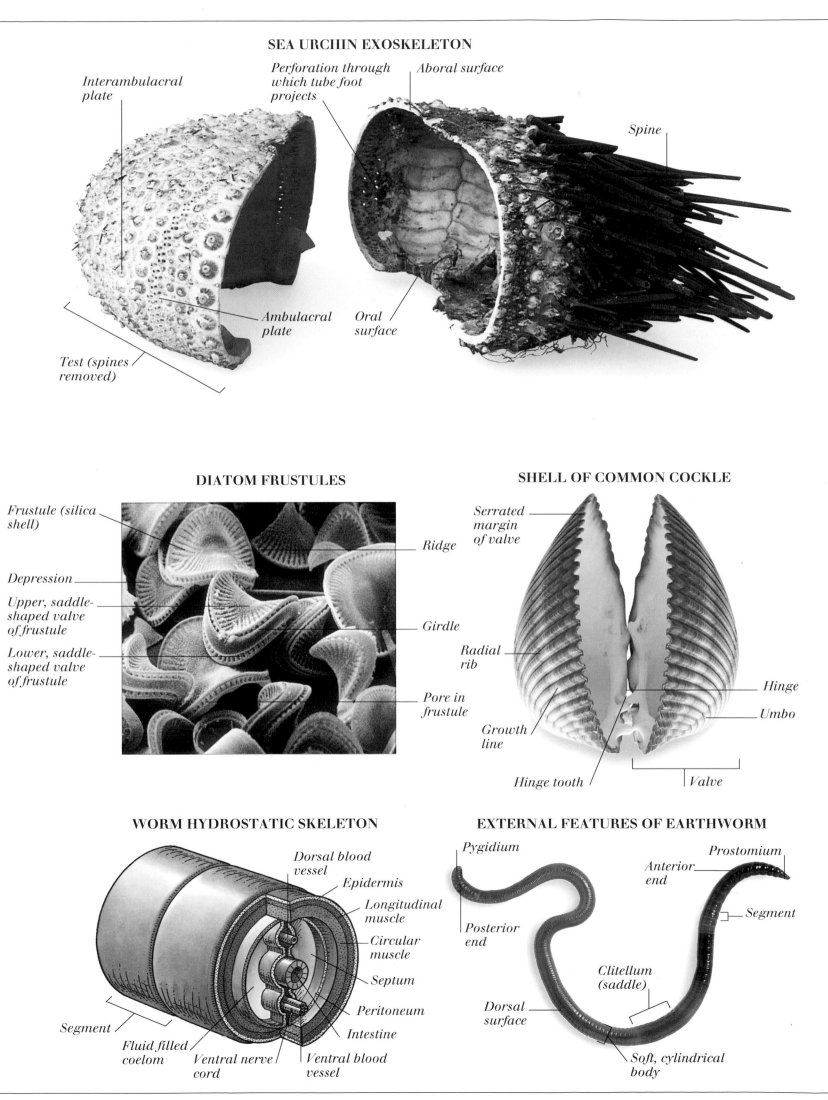

SEA URCHIN EXOSKELETON

Interambulacral plate

Perforation through which tube foot projects

Aboral surface

Spine

Ambulacral plate

Oral surface

Test (spines removed)

DIATOM FRUSTULES

Frustule (silica shell)

Depression

Upper, saddle-shaped valve of frustule

Lower, saddle-shaped valve of frustule

Ridge

Girdle

Pore in frustule

SHELL OF COMMON COCKLE

Serrated margin of valve

Radial rib

Growth line

Hinge

Umbo

Hinge tooth

Valve

WORM HYDROSTATIC SKELETON

Dorsal blood vessel

Epidermis

Longitudinal muscle

Circular muscle

Septum

Peritoneum

Intestine

Ventral blood vessel

Segment

Fluid filled coelom

Ventral nerve cord

EXTERNAL FEATURES OF EARTHWORM

Pygidium

Prostomium

Anterior end

Posterior end

Clitellum (saddle)

Dorsal surface

Soft, cylindrical body

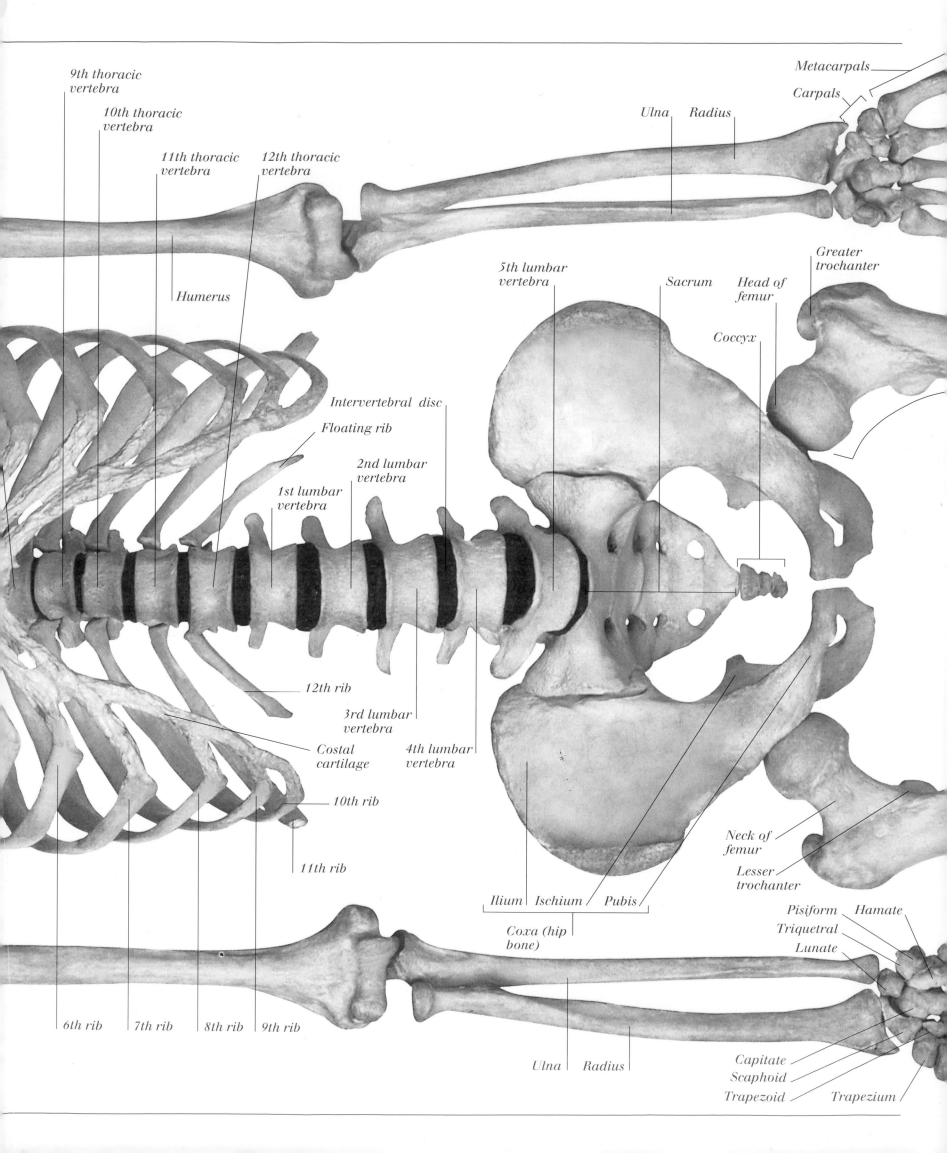

9th thoracic
vertebra

10th thoracic
vertebra

11th thoracic
vertebra

12th thoracic
vertebra

Humerus

Metacarpals

Carpals

Ulna   Radius

5th lumbar
vertebra

Sacrum

Head of
femur

Greater
trochanter

Coccyx

Intervertebral disc

Floating rib

2nd lumbar
vertebra

1st lumbar
vertebra

12th rib

3rd lumbar
vertebra

Costal
cartilage

4th lumbar
vertebra

10th rib

11th rib

Neck of
femur

Lesser
trochanter

Ilium   Ischium   Pubis

Coxa (hip
bone)

Pisiform   Hamate

Triquetral

Lunate

6th rib   7th rib   8th rib   9th rib

Ulna   Radius

Capitate

Scaphoid

Trapezoid   Trapezium

The human skeleton

HUMANS HAVE A BONY ENDOSKELETON made up of 206 bones (we are born with up to 300, but many of these fuse during childhood). The skeleton is divided into two parts: the axial and the appendicular skeleton. The axial skeleton, which consists of the skull, backbone, and ribcage, forms the upright axis of the body. It helps to protect the brain, spinal cord, and organs in the chest. The appendicular skeleton consists of the upper and lower limbs, and the pectoral (shoulder) and pelvic (hip) girdles. The human pelvis is adapted for an upright stance. The lower limbs support the upper body and enable walking and other locomotory movements to take place, whereas the upper limbs are used for manipulation.

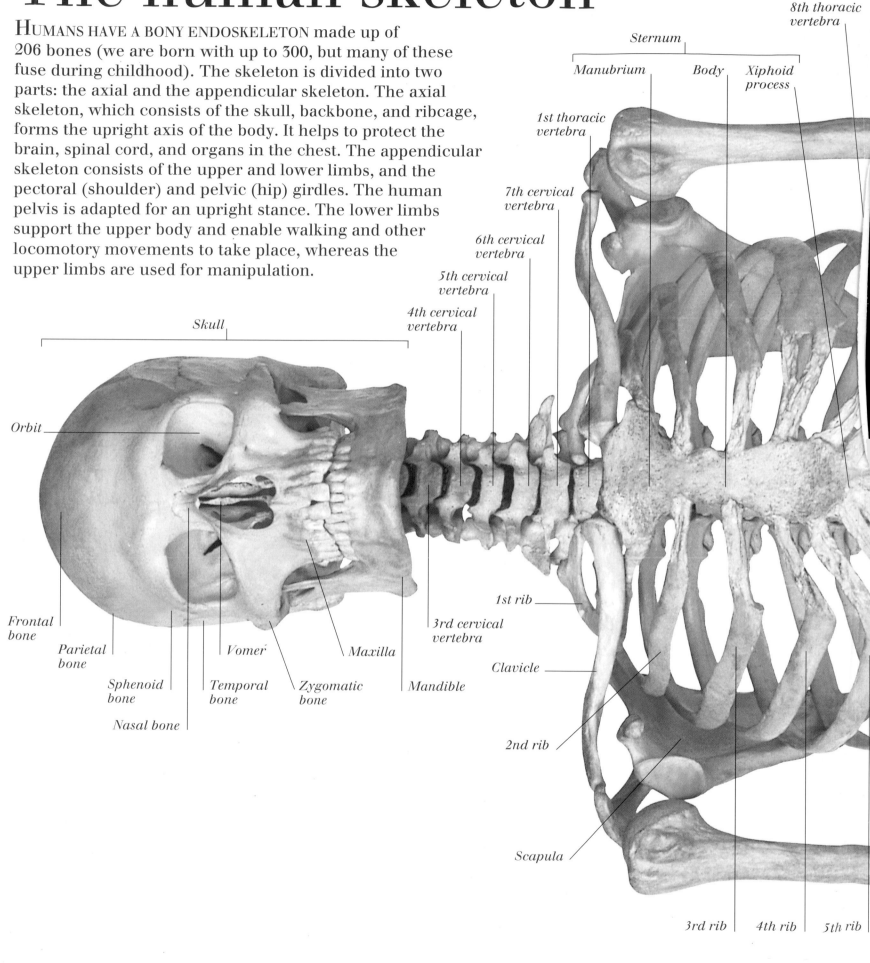

The human skeleton through life

THE SKELETON OF THE HUMAN FETUS is formed from tough but flexible cartilage that acts as a blueprint for bone construction. During ossification (changing to bone), which begins before birth, the cartilage is broken down and the resulting space is filled by bone-building mineral salts and protein fibres secreted by bone cells. At birth, the diaphyses (shafts) of the long bones are already ossified, while the epiphyses (ends of bones) are still cartilaginous. The epiphyses gradually ossify, leaving a cartilaginous epiphyseal plate (growth plate) where growth continues until late adolescence. The bones of the skull are formed by the ossification of fibrous tissue, rather than cartilage. In the newborn baby, this flexible tissue forms fontanelles between the partly ossified skull bones, allowing the cranium to enlarge as the brain grows. The facial bones also enlarge as the skull develops. After the age of about 40, bone mass starts to decrease, a process that is sometimes accelerated by osteoporosis.

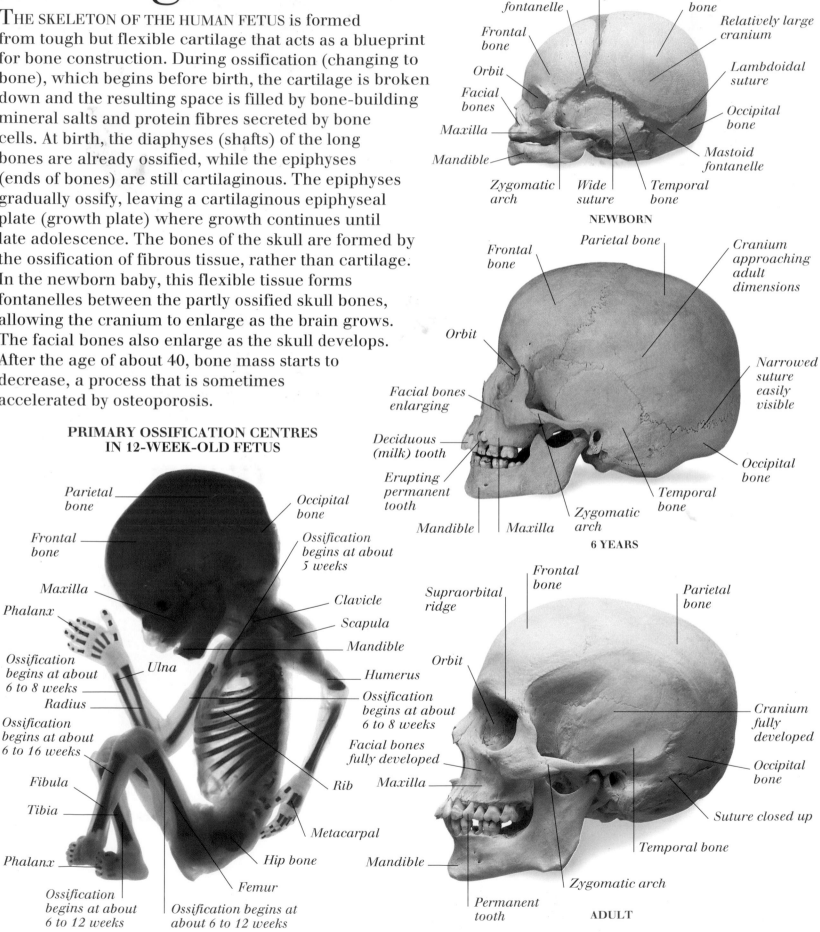

GROWTH OF HUMAN SKULL

Sphenoidal fontanelle
Anterior fontanelle
Parietal bone
Frontal bone
Relatively large cranium
Orbit
Lambdoidal suture
Facial bones
Occipital bone
Maxilla
Mastoid fontanelle
Mandible
Zygomatic arch
Wide suture
Temporal bone

NEWBORN

Frontal bone
Parietal bone
Cranium approaching adult dimensions
Orbit
Narrowed suture easily visible
Facial bones enlarging
Deciduous (milk) tooth
Erupting permanent tooth
Occipital bone
Mandible
Maxilla
Zygomatic arch
Temporal bone

6 YEARS

PRIMARY OSSIFICATION CENTRES IN 12-WEEK-OLD FETUS

Parietal bone
Occipital bone
Frontal bone
Ossification begins at about 5 weeks
Maxilla
Phalanx
Clavicle
Scapula
Mandible
Ossification begins at about 6 to 8 weeks
Ulna
Humerus
Radius
Ossification begins at about 6 to 8 weeks
Ossification begins at about 6 to 16 weeks
Facial bones fully developed
Fibula
Maxilla
Rib
Tibia
Metacarpal
Phalanx
Hip bone
Femur
Mandible
Ossification begins at about 6 to 12 weeks
Ossification begins at about 6 to 12 weeks
Permanent tooth

Supraorbital ridge
Frontal bone
Parietal bone
Orbit
Cranium fully developed
Occipital bone
Suture closed up
Temporal bone
Zygomatic arch

ADULT

BONE DEVELOPMENT IN HUMAN HAND

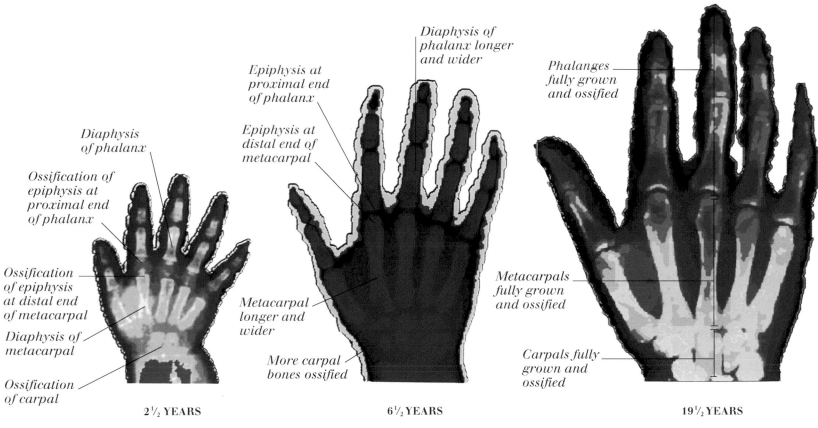

Diaphysis of phalanx longer and wider

Epiphysis at proximal end of phalanx

Epiphysis at distal end of metacarpal

Phalanges fully grown and ossified

Diaphysis of phalanx

Ossification of epiphysis at proximal end of phalanx

Ossification of epiphysis at distal end of metacarpal

Diaphysis of metacarpal

Ossification of carpal

Metacarpal longer and wider

More carpal bones ossified

Metacarpals fully grown and ossified

Carpals fully grown and ossified

2¹⁄₂ YEARS

6¹⁄₂ YEARS

19¹⁄₂ YEARS

SCANNING ELECTRON MICROGRAPH OF CANCELLOUS BONE

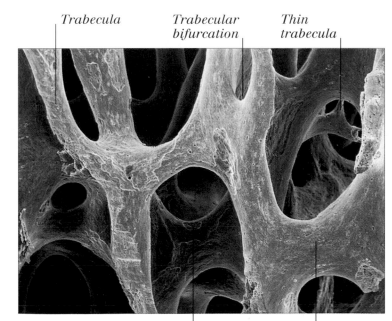

Trabecula

Trabecular bifurcation

Thin trabecula

Marrow space between trabeculae

Thick trabecula

HEALTHY BONE

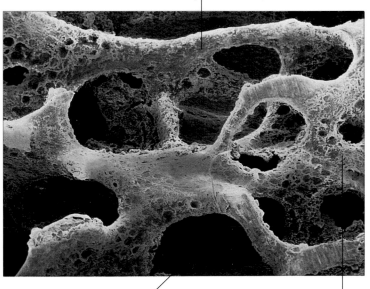

Fewer trabeculae

Marrow space between trabeculae enlarged

Porous surface of trabecula weakened by loss of bone

BONE WITH OSTEOPOROSIS

Plant skeletons

SKELETON OF
MAGNOLIA
LEAF

PLANTS TYPICALLY HAVE A STEM that bears leaves and flowers, and roots that anchor the plant in the soil. The stem and roots are supported and protected by a skeletal system. The skeleton of the stem helps the plant to resist bending caused by external forces; it also holds the leaves in position so that they can receive the sunlight necessary for photosynthesis. The stems of herbaceous (non-woody) plants are supported by cells called sclerenchyma and collenchyma, and by strong-walled, water-conducting cells called xylem. In woody plants, the trunks and branches are supported by an inner core of xylem and associated fibres, which together form the wood. As the wood in the centre of the tree gets older, it loses its conductive role but continues to support the stem. This non-conducting wood is known as heartwood. The outer, conducting wood is known as sapwood. Roots have a central cylinder of transport tissue, known as the stele. The stele contains tough xylem that enables roots to resist the pressure produced as they grow through the soil.

MICROGRAPH OF XYLEM IN BUTTERCUP STEM

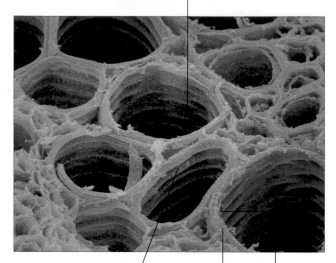

Lumen of xylem vessel

Annular thickening in wall of xylem vessel

Lignified cell wall of xylem vessel

Xylem vessel

LONGITUDINAL SECTION THROUGH BUTTERCUP ROOT

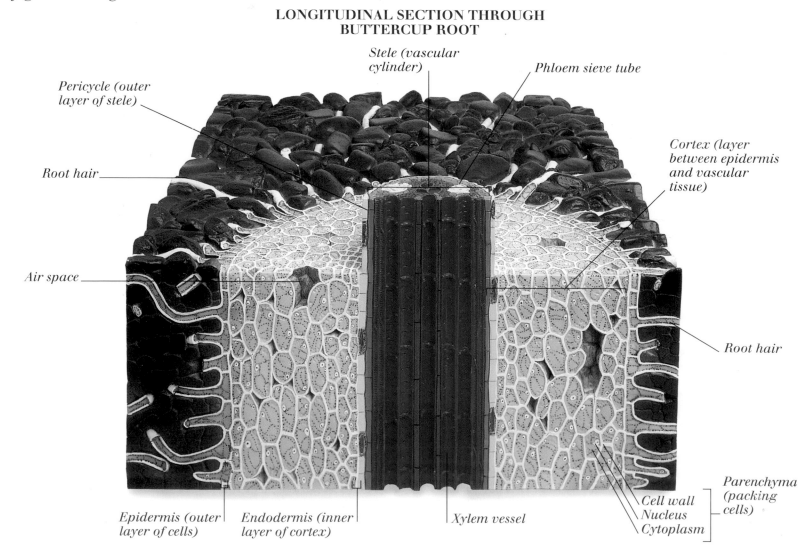

Stele (vascular cylinder)

Phloem sieve tube

Pericycle (outer layer of stele)

Cortex (layer between epidermis and vascular tissue)

Root hair

Air space

Root hair

Epidermis (outer layer of cells)

Endodermis (inner layer of cortex)

Xylem vessel

Cell wall
Nucleus
Cytoplasm

Parenchyma (packing cells)

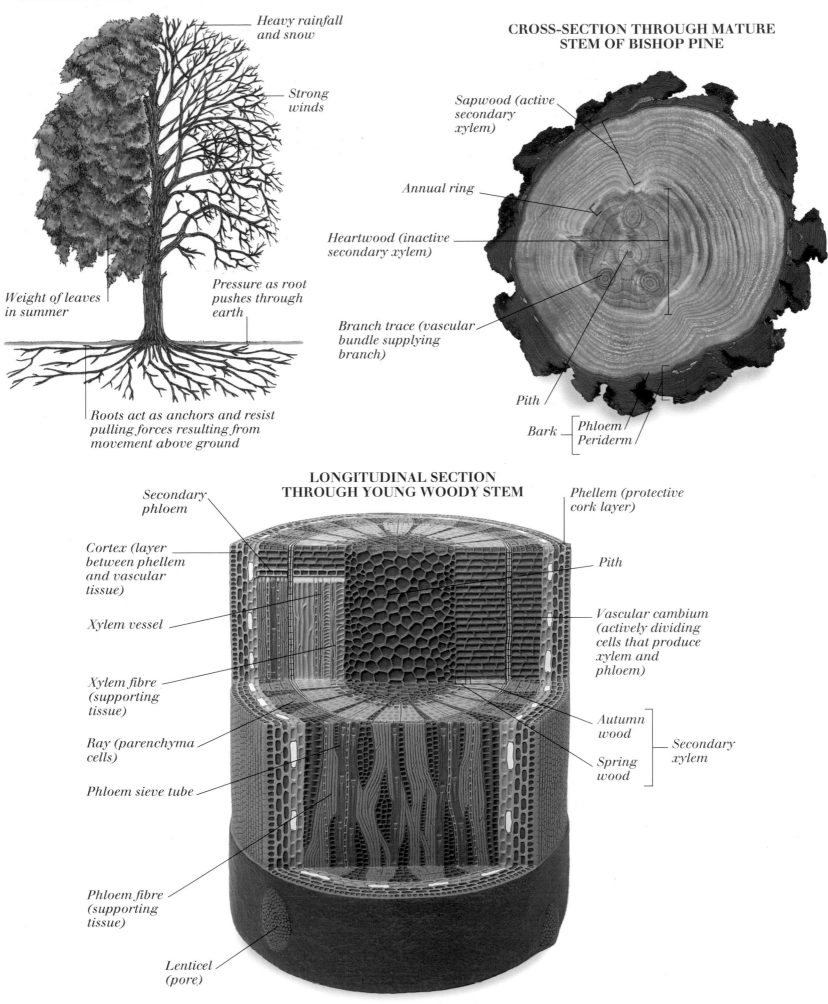

TREE SHOWING EXTERNAL STRESSES

Heavy rainfall and snow

Strong winds

Weight of leaves in summer

Pressure as root pushes through earth

Roots act as anchors and resist pulling forces resulting from movement above ground

CROSS-SECTION THROUGH MATURE STEM OF BISHOP PINE

Sapwood (active secondary xylem)

Annual ring

Heartwood (inactive secondary xylem)

Branch trace (vascular bundle supplying branch)

Pith

Bark { *Phloem* / *Periderm*

LONGITUDINAL SECTION THROUGH YOUNG WOODY STEM

Secondary phloem

Cortex (layer between phellem and vascular tissue)

Xylem vessel

Xylem fibre (supporting tissue)

Ray (parenchyma cells)

Phloem sieve tube

Phloem fibre (supporting tissue)

Lenticel (pore)

Phellem (protective cork layer)

Pith

Vascular cambium (actively dividing cells that produce xylem and phloem)

Autumn wood

Spring wood

Secondary xylem

Shells and simple skeletons

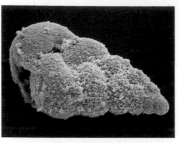

FOSSIL FORAMINIFERAN

SHELLS ARE EXOSKELETONS that protect the soft bodies of most molluscs. Each mollusc group has a characteristic shell form. Gastropods, such as the lightning whelk, have a cone-shaped, spiral shell, made up of tubular whorls, with an aperture through which the animal's head is extended or retracted. Bivalves, such as the mussel, have a hinged shell with two halves, that are opened and closed by powerful muscles. Cephalopods, such as the octopus, generally lack external shells. However, one cephalopod, *Nautilus*, has a flat-spiral shell, divided into chambers. *Nautilus* occupies only the body chamber. Some invertebrates have simple exoskeletons. Corals, for example, are colonial invertebrates that build protective calcium carbonate cases into which they can retreat. Foraminiferans are aquatic protozoans with a shell that protects their amoeboid body.

EXTERNAL FEATURES OF NAUTILUS

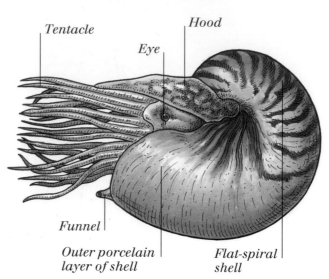

Tentacle

Hood

Eye

Funnel

Outer porcelain layer of shell

Flat-spiral shell

SECTION THROUGH NAUTILUS SHELL

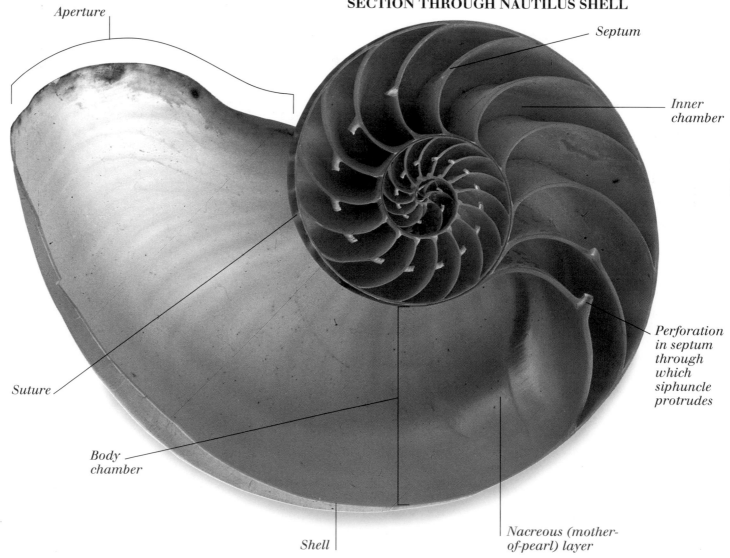

Aperture

Septum

Inner chamber

Suture

Perforation in septum through which siphuncle protrudes

Body chamber

Nacreous (mother-of-pearl) layer

Shell

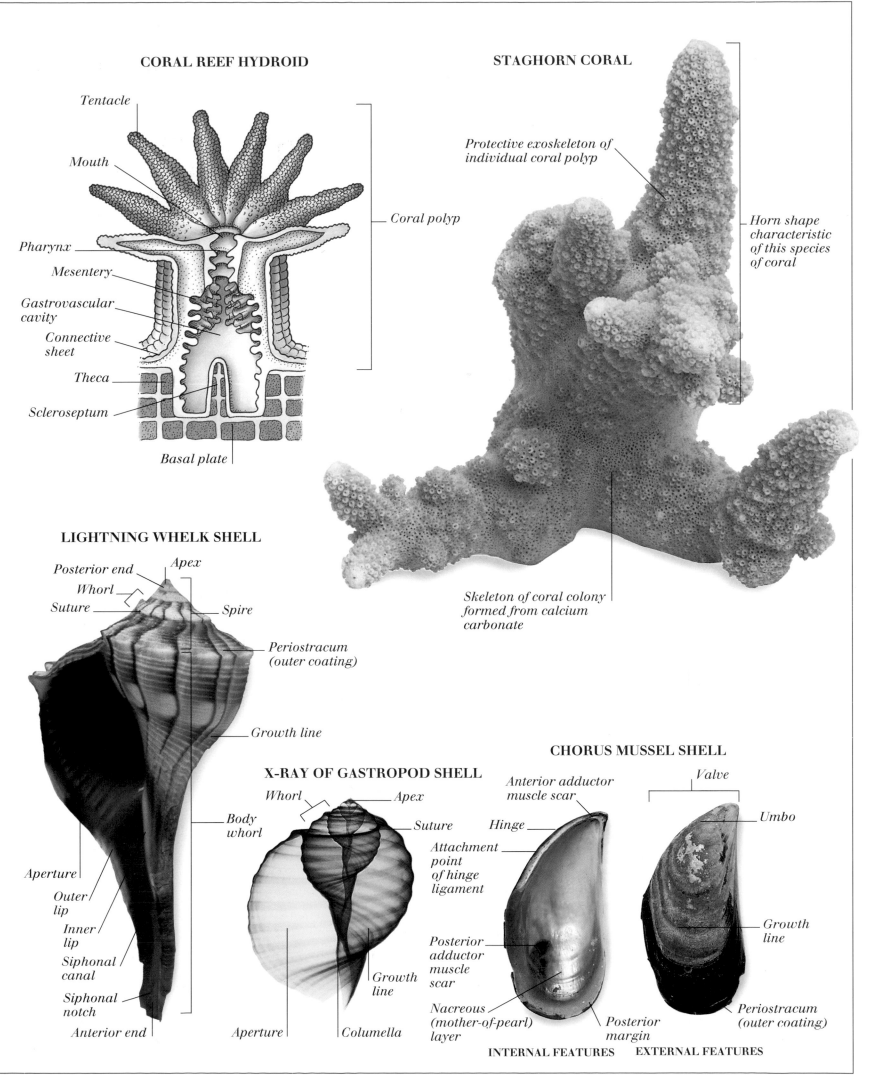

CORAL REEF HYDROID

Tentacle

Mouth

Pharynx

Mesentery

Gastrovascular cavity

Connective sheet

Theca

Scleroseptum

Basal plate

Coral polyp

STAGHORN CORAL

Protective exoskeleton of individual coral polyp

Horn shape characteristic of this species of coral

Skeleton of coral colony formed from calcium carbonate

LIGHTNING WHELK SHELL

Posterior end

Whorl

Suture

Apex

Spire

Periostracum (outer coating)

Growth line

Body whorl

Aperture

Outer lip

Inner lip

Siphonal canal

Siphonal notch

Anterior end

X-RAY OF GASTROPOD SHELL

Whorl

Apex

Suture

Growth line

Aperture

Columella

CHORUS MUSSEL SHELL

Anterior adductor muscle scar

Valve

Hinge

Attachment point of hinge ligament

Umbo

Posterior adductor muscle scar

Nacreous (mother-of-pearl) layer

Posterior margin

Growth line

Periostracum (outer coating)

INTERNAL FEATURES

EXTERNAL FEATURES

19

Arthropod exoskeletons

TARANTULA MOULT

MOST ANIMALS WITH exoskeletons belong to the arthropod group (animals with jointed limbs), which includes insects, such as beetles; arachnids, such as scorpions; and crustaceans, such as crabs. The arthropod exoskeleton, also known as the cuticle, encases the entire body (including the eyes), and consists of inflexible plates that meet at flexible joints. The joints are formed by thinner sections of cuticle called articular membranes. Muscles, attached to the exoskeleton across these joints, contract to produce movement. The arthropod exoskeleton cannot expand, and must be moulted periodically to allow the animal to grow. An exoskeleton also imposes a maximum size on arthropods: although the cuticle contains a substance called chitin that makes it both hard and light, above a certain body size the cuticle becomes so heavy that movement is impossible.

WALKING MECHANISM OF INSECT

Protractor muscle (pulls limb forwards)
Cuticle
Flexor muscle (pulls limb downwards)
Retractor muscle (pulls limb backwards)
Notum
Pleuron
Sternum
Extensor muscle (pulls limb upwards)
Limb
Joint

MECHANISM IN BODY

Extensor muscle (straightens joint)
Articular membrane
Condyle
Cuticle
Flexor muscle bends joint

MECHANISM IN LEG

SCORPION EXOSKELETON

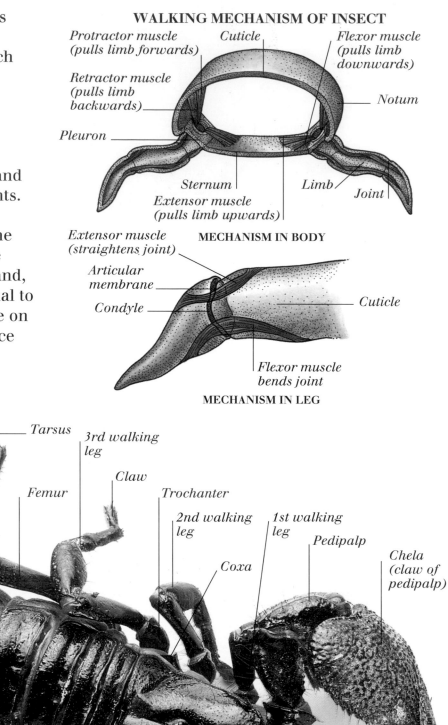

Tarsus
Metatarsus
Tibia
Patella
4th walking leg
3rd walking leg
Claw
Femur
Trochanter
2nd walking leg
1st walking leg
Pedipalp
Coxa
Chela (claw of pedipalp)
Metasoma (tail section of opisthosoma)
Chelicera
Aculeus (sting)
Telson
Stinging apparatus
Opisthosoma (abdomen)
Prosoma (cephalothorax)
Median eye

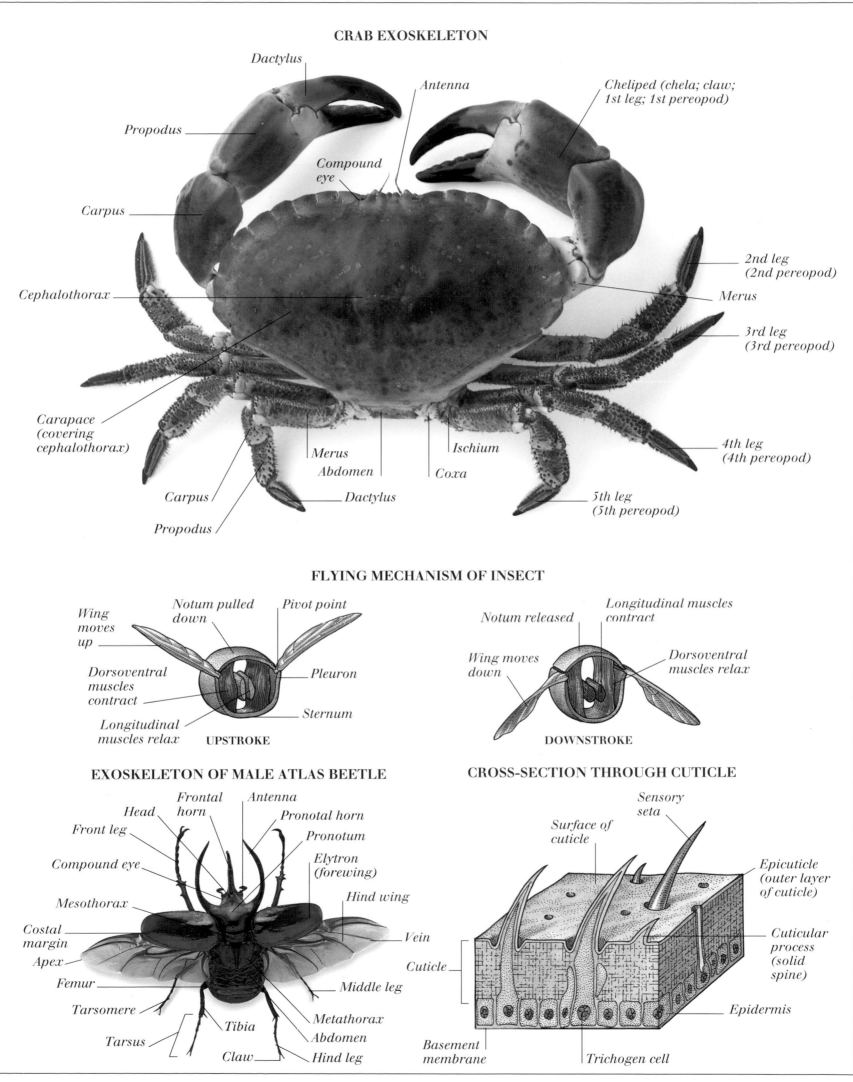

CRAB EXOSKELETON

Dactylus

Antenna

Cheliped (chela; claw; 1st leg; 1st pereopod)

Propodus

Compound eye

Carpus

Cephalothorax

2nd leg (2nd pereopod)

Merus

3rd leg (3rd pereopod)

Carapace (covering cephalothorax)

Carpus

Merus

Abdomen

Ischium

Coxa

4th leg (4th pereopod)

Propodus

Dactylus

5th leg (5th pereopod)

FLYING MECHANISM OF INSECT

Wing moves up

Notum pulled down

Pivot point

Dorsoventral muscles contract

Pleuron

Longitudinal muscles relax

Sternum

UPSTROKE

Notum released

Longitudinal muscles contract

Wing moves down

Dorsoventral muscles relax

DOWNSTROKE

EXOSKELETON OF MALE ATLAS BEETLE

Head

Frontal horn

Antenna

Front leg

Pronotal horn

Compound eye

Pronotum

Elytron (forewing)

Mesothorax

Hind wing

Costal margin

Vein

Apex

Femur

Middle leg

Tarsomere

Metathorax

Tarsus

Tibia

Abdomen

Claw

Hind leg

CROSS-SECTION THROUGH CUTICLE

Sensory seta

Surface of cuticle

Epicuticle (outer layer of cuticle)

Cuticle

Cuticular process (solid spine)

Epidermis

Basement membrane

Trichogen cell

Fish skeletons

FISHES WERE THE FIRST VERTEBRATES to evolve, and the first animals to have endoskeletons (internal skeletons). Bony fishes, such as cod and salmon, have a skeleton made of bone, as do most other vertebrates. Cartilaginous fishes, such as sharks (including dogfish) and rays, have a skeleton made of cartilage: a strong, flexible material that is also found in the human ear and nose. The fish skeleton produces a streamlined shape, adapting the animal for movement in water. It also has fins for propelling, stabilizing, and steering. The tapering skull minimizes drag as the fish moves forwards, and supports and protects the brain and gills. The flexible backbone (vertebral column) has muscles attached on either side along its length. These muscles contract alternately, bending the body from side to side to propel the fish forwards through the water. The fins, including the tail, are supported by bones and rods. The dorsal and ventral fins, positioned on the midline, prevent the fish from rolling; the paired pectoral and pelvic fins allow it to control its direction.

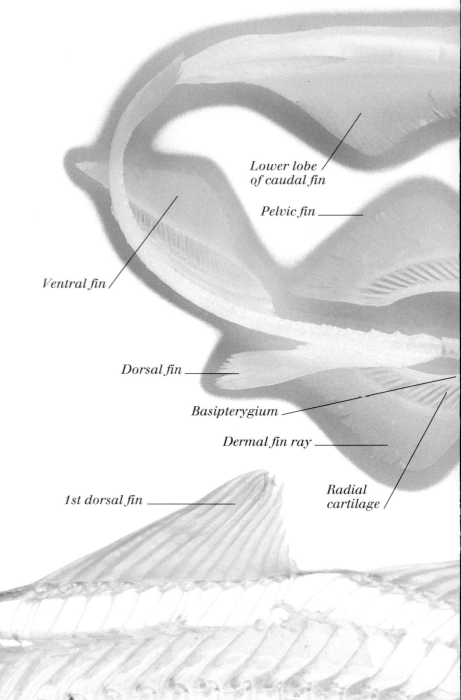

Lower lobe of caudal fin

Pelvic fin

Ventral fin

Dorsal fin

Basipterygium

Dermal fin ray

Radial cartilage

1st dorsal fin

COD SKELETON

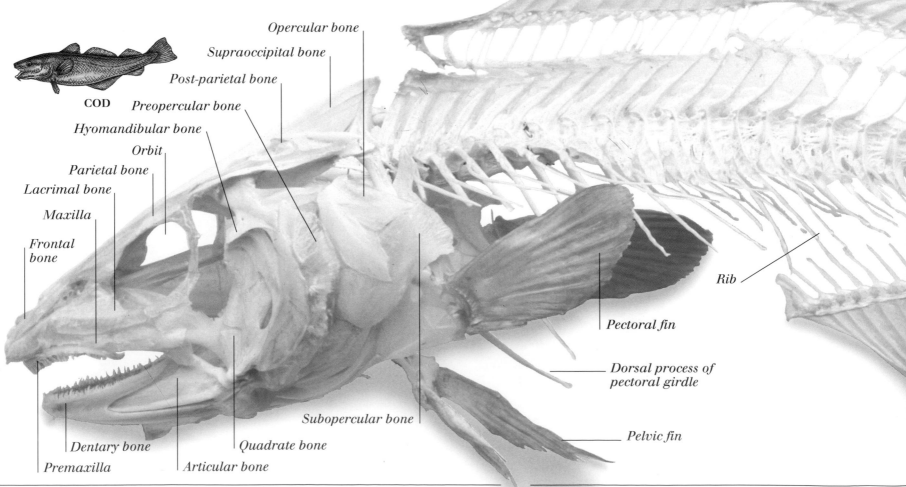

COD

Opercular bone

Supraoccipital bone

Post-parietal bone

Preopercular bone

Hyomandibular bone

Orbit

Parietal bone

Lacrimal bone

Maxilla

Frontal bone

Rib

Pectoral fin

Dorsal process of pectoral girdle

Pelvic fin

Dentary bone

Premaxilla

Quadrate bone

Articular bone

Subopercular bone

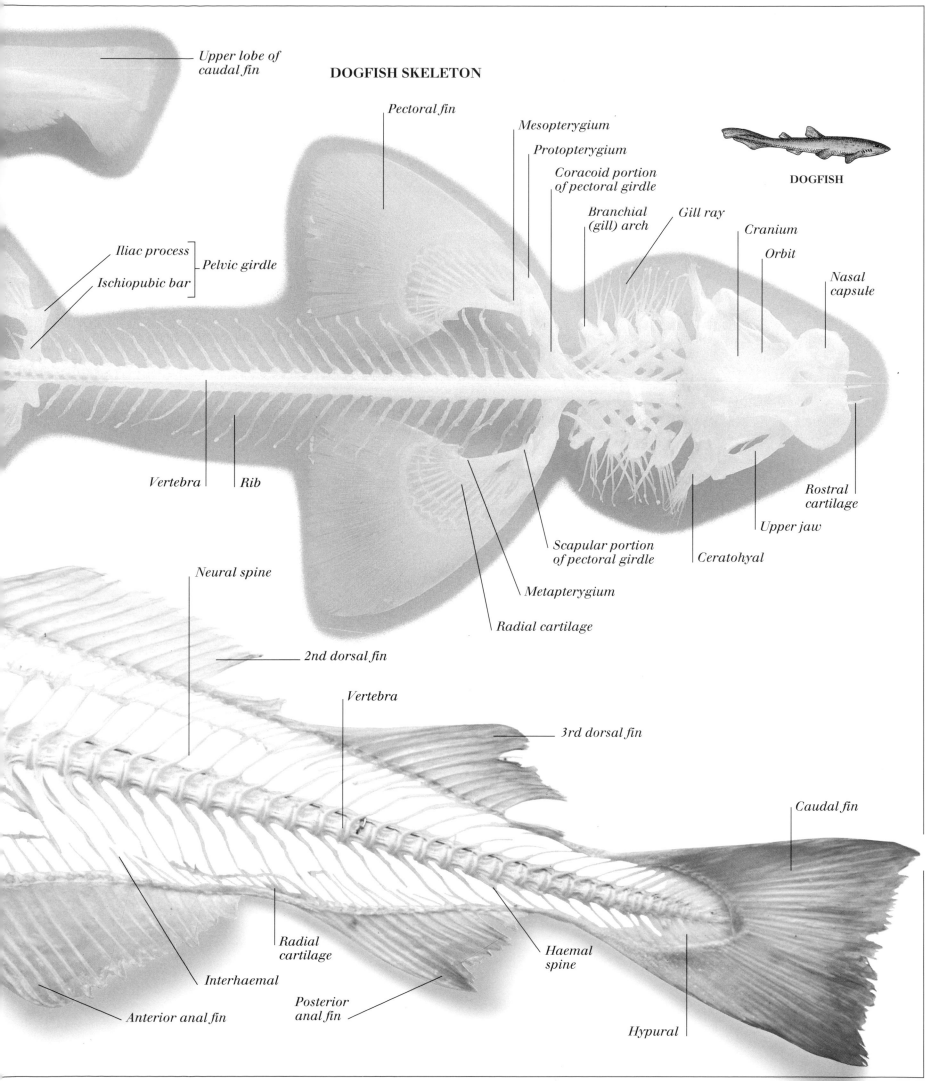

DOGFISH SKELETON

Upper lobe of caudal fin

Pectoral fin

Mesopterygium

Protopterygium

Coracoid portion of pectoral girdle

Branchial (gill) arch

Gill ray

Cranium

Orbit

Nasal capsule

DOGFISH

Iliac process

Ischiopubic bar

Pelvic girdle

Vertebra

Rib

Scapular portion of pectoral girdle

Ceratohyal

Upper jaw

Rostral cartilage

Metapterygium

Radial cartilage

Neural spine

2nd dorsal fin

Vertebra

3rd dorsal fin

Caudal fin

Radial cartilage

Haemal spine

Interhaemal

Anterior anal fin

Posterior anal fin

Hypural

Amphibian skeletons

AMPHIBIANS ARE VERTEBRATES that typically are adapted for life both on land and in water. They generally have a bony endoskeleton, although some species of salamander have mainly cartilaginous pectoral (shoulder) and pelvic (hip) girdles. The three amphibian groups show considerable skeletal variation. Frogs and toads have a short, squat body; a broad skull with a wide mouth and large orbits; and long hind limbs and feet for jumping and swimming. The large pelvic girdle transmits force from the hind legs to the rest of the body through a short, inflexible backbone. Typically, the pectoral girdle is strengthened to withstand the force of landing. Salamanders have elongated bodies with tails; a flexible backbone that curves from side to side during movement on land or in water; short front and hind legs; and a broad skull. The third amphibian group, the caecilians, are adapted for burrowing. Their limbless skeletons have a compact skull with no orbits, and a long, flexible backbone with up to 100 vertebrae.

SALAMANDER SKELETON

Premaxilla

Maxilla

Frontal bone

Orbit

Parietal bone

Metacarpal

Phalanx

Cervical vertebra

Carpal

Ulna

Humerus

Radius

Elbow joint

Scapulocoracoid

Thoracic vertebra

Rib

Metatarsal

Tibia

Sacral vertebra

Fibula

Femur

Knee joint

Ilium

Tarsal

Caudal vertebra

Phalanx

CAECILIAN SKELETON

Rib

Cervical vertebra

Thick skull

Nasal bone

Vertebra

Parietal bone

Frontal bone

CAECILIAN

SALAMANDER

FROG SKELETON

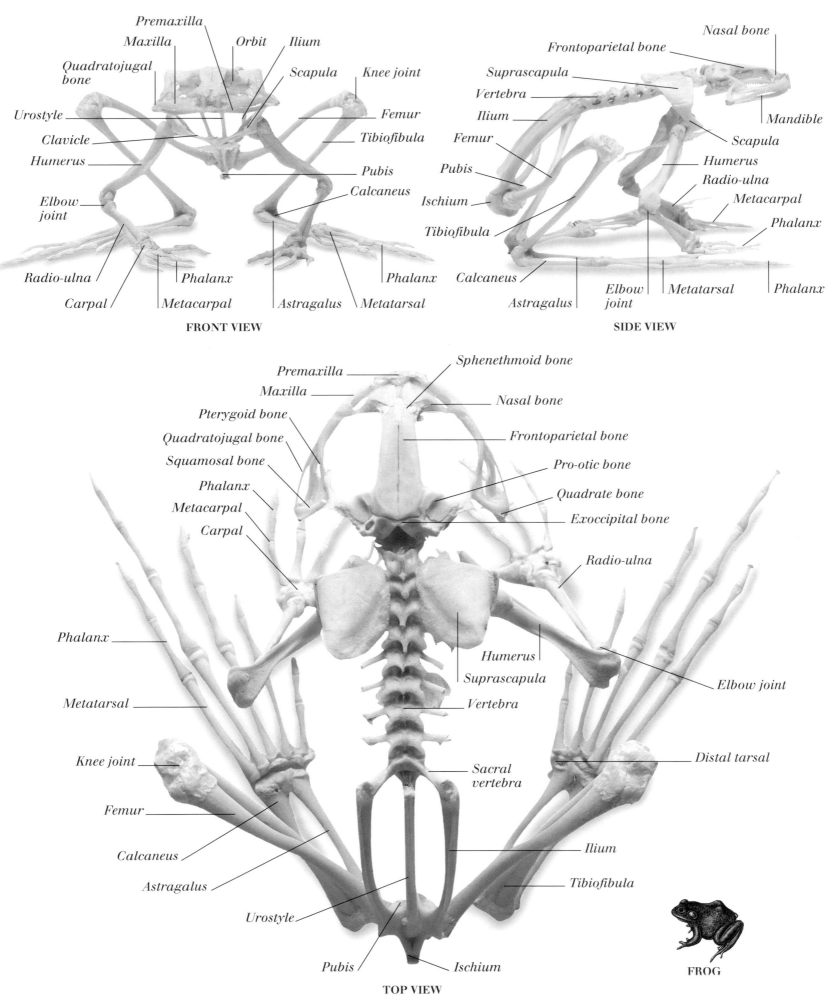

FRONT VIEW

Premaxilla
Maxilla
Quadratojugal bone
Orbit
Ilium
Scapula
Knee joint
Urostyle
Clavicle
Femur
Humerus
Tibiofibula
Elbow joint
Pubis
Calcaneus
Radio-ulna
Phalanx
Carpal
Metacarpal
Astragalus
Metatarsal
Phalanx

SIDE VIEW

Nasal bone
Frontoparietal bone
Suprascapula
Vertebra
Ilium
Femur
Scapula
Mandible
Pubis
Humerus
Ischium
Radio-ulna
Metacarpal
Tibiofibula
Phalanx
Calcaneus
Astragalus
Elbow joint
Metatarsal
Phalanx

TOP VIEW

Premaxilla
Maxilla
Sphenethmoid bone
Pterygoid bone
Nasal bone
Quadratojugal bone
Frontoparietal bone
Squamosal bone
Pro-otic bone
Phalanx
Quadrate bone
Metacarpal
Exoccipital bone
Carpal
Radio-ulna
Phalanx
Humerus
Suprascapula
Metatarsal
Vertebra
Elbow joint
Knee joint
Femur
Sacral vertebra
Distal tarsal
Calcaneus
Astragalus
Ilium
Urostyle
Tibiofibula
Pubis
Ischium

FROG

TOP VIEW

Reptile skeletons 1

REPTILES ARE VERTEBRATES with a bony endoskeleton. Typically, the reptile skeleton is elongated, with a flexible backbone and short legs that project sideways. However, skeletal variations occur within the group. For example, snakes lack limbs but have a long backbone consisting of between about 180 and 400 vertebrae. Snakes also have a highly flexible jaw mechanism, allowing large prey to be swallowed whole. Turtles have both an exoskeleton and an endoskeleton. The exoskeleton consists of a shell with an outer, horny layer and an inner, bony layer. The ribs, backbone, pectoral (shoulder) and pelvic (hip) girdles of the endoskeleton are fused to the inner layer of the exoskeleton. Crocodilians, such as the gharial and the Nile crocodile, are semi-aquatic reptiles with a long tail for swimming; a long snout with pointed teeth, and nostrils and eye sockets set high on the skull. Lizards generally follow the typical reptile body plan, but many also have features adapted to their environment, such as the tree-dwelling chameleon, which has opposable toes and a prehensile tail for grasping branches. Lizard-like tuataras retain primitive reptilian features, such as two complete temporal fenestrae (openings in the skull) and teeth that are fused to the jaw.

SNAKE SKELETON

Rib

Vertebra

Skull   Orbit

SNAKE

Caudal vertebra

SNAKE SKULL   Orbit

Frontal bone

Premaxilla

Parietal bone

Maxilla

Supratemporal bone

Postfrontal bone

Quadrate bone

Ectopterygoid bone

Pterygoid bone

Articular bone

Surangular bone

Dentary bone

GHARIAL SKULL

Articular bone

Parietal bone

Squamosal bone

Infratemporal fenestra

Quadrate bone

Frontal bone

Postorbital bone

Orbit   Maxilla   Premaxilla

Jugal bone

Surangular bone

Angular bone

Mandibular fenestra   Dentary bone   Mandible   Naris

GHARIAL

Caudal vertebrae

Lumbar vertebrae

Sacrum

Rib

Ilium   Ischium

Tarsals

Metatarsals   Pubis   Femur

Fibula   Tibia   Phalanges

NILE CROCODILE

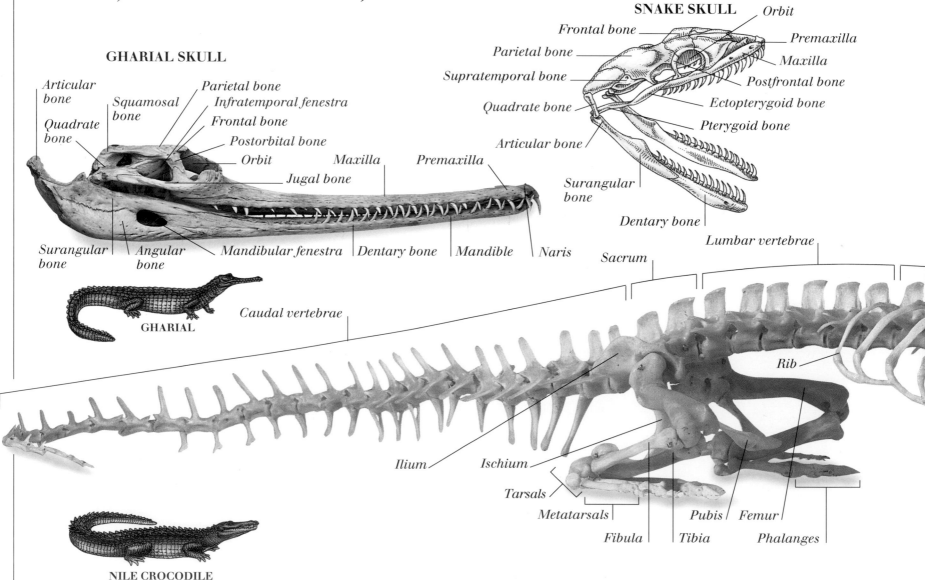

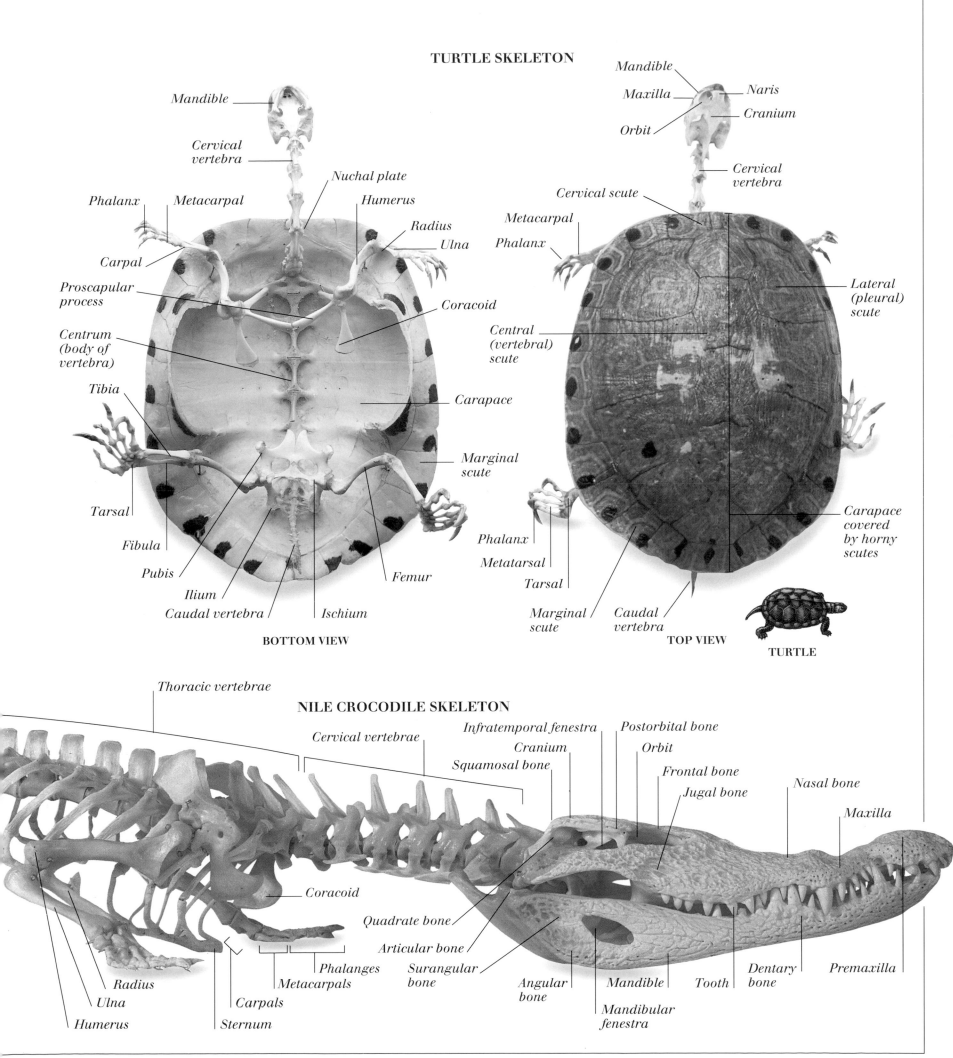

TURTLE SKELETON

BOTTOM VIEW

Mandible

Cervical
vertebra

Phalanx

Metacarpal

Nuchal plate

Humerus

Radius

Ulna

Carpal

Proscapular
process

Coracoid

Centrum
(body of
vertebra)

Carapace

Tibia

Marginal
scute

Tarsal

Fibula

Pubis

Ilium

Caudal vertebra

Ischium

Femur

Mandible

Maxilla

Naris

Orbit

Cranium

Cervical
vertebra

Cervical scute

Metacarpal

Phalanx

Lateral
(pleural)
scute

Central
(vertebral)
scute

Carapace
covered
by horny
scutes

Phalanx

Metatarsal

Tarsal

Marginal
scute

Caudal
vertebra

TOP VIEW

TURTLE

NILE CROCODILE SKELETON

Thoracic vertebrae

Cervical vertebrae

Infratemporal fenestra

Postorbital bone

Cranium

Orbit

Squamosal bone

Frontal bone

Jugal bone

Nasal bone

Maxilla

Coracoid

Quadrate bone

Articular bone

Surangular
bone

Angular
bone

Mandible

Tooth

Dentary
bone

Premaxilla

Radius

Ulna

Humerus

Carpals

Metacarpals

Phalanges

Sternum

Mandibular
fenestra

Reptile skeletons 2

MONITOR LIZARD SKELETON

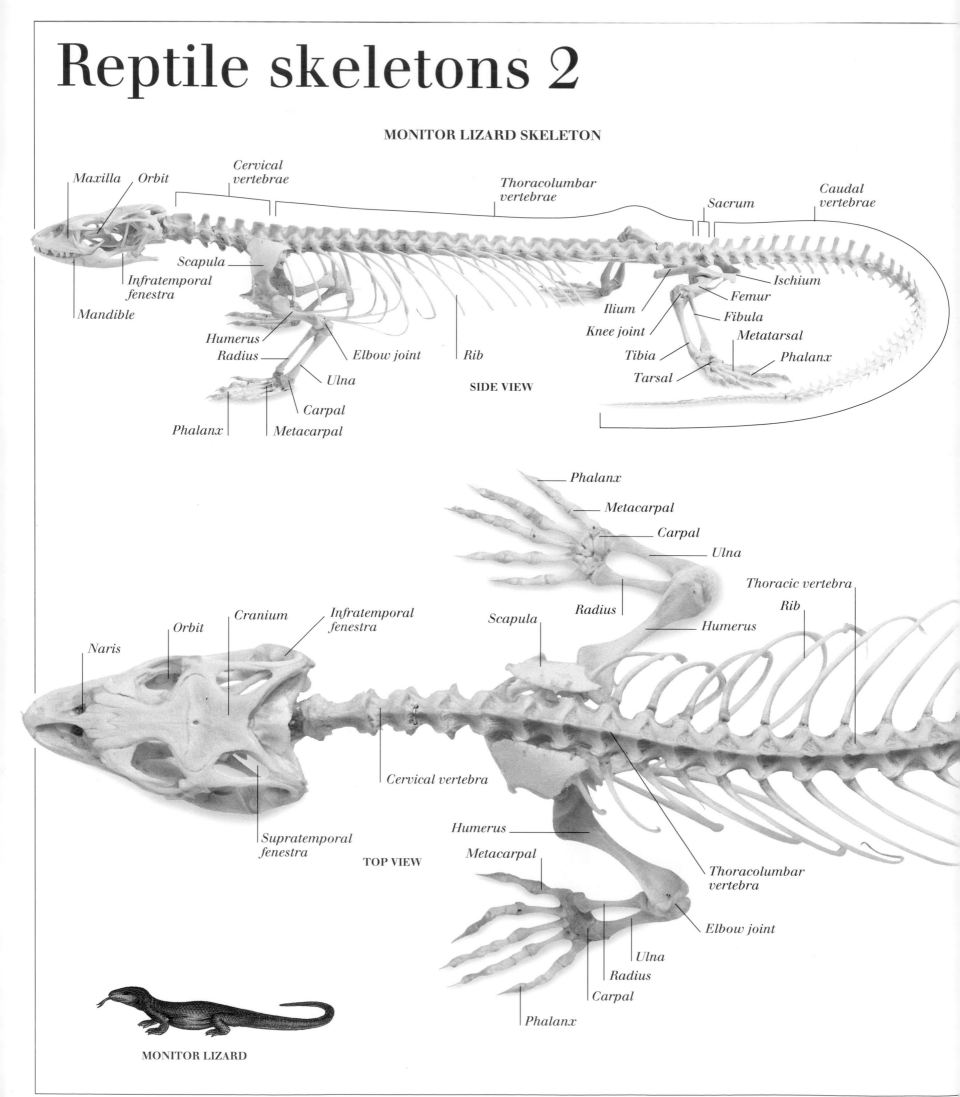

Maxilla   *Orbit*   *Cervical vertebrae*   *Thoracolumbar vertebrae*   *Sacrum*   *Caudal vertebrae*

Infratemporal fenestra

Mandible

Scapula

Humerus
Radius   *Elbow joint*   *Rib*

Ulna

Carpal

Phalanx   *Metacarpal*

Ischium
Femur
Ilium   *Fibula*
Knee joint   *Metatarsal*
Tibia   *Phalanx*
Tarsal

SIDE VIEW

Phalanx

Metacarpal

Carpal

Ulna

Naris   *Orbit*   *Cranium*   *Infratemporal fenestra*   *Scapula*   *Radius*   *Thoracic vertebra*   *Rib*

Humerus

Cervical vertebra

Supratemporal fenestra

TOP VIEW

Humerus
Metacarpal

Thoracolumbar vertebra

Elbow joint

Ulna
Radius
Carpal

Phalanx

MONITOR LIZARD

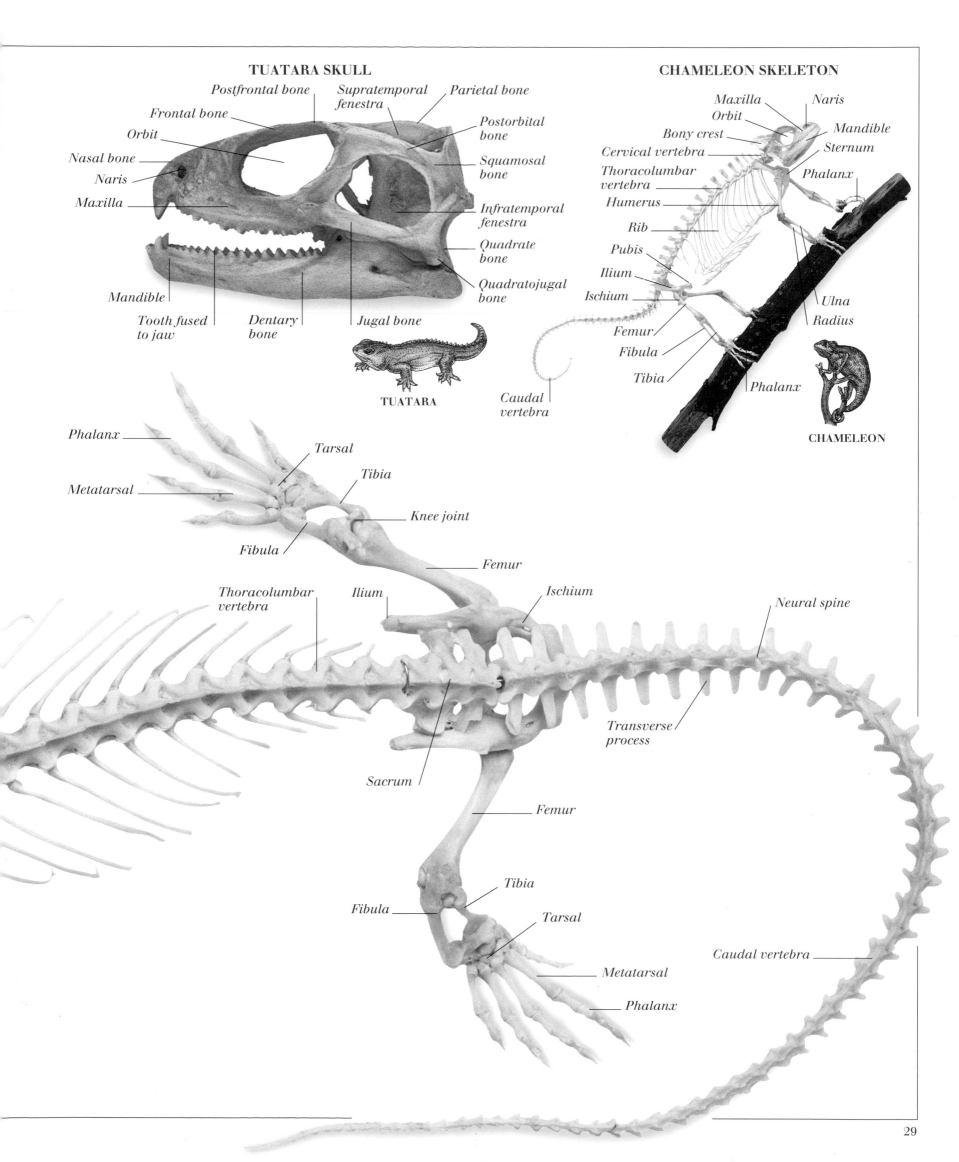

TUATARA SKULL

Postfrontal bone
Supratemporal fenestra
Parietal bone
Frontal bone
Orbit
Postorbital bone
Nasal bone
Naris
Squamosal bone
Maxilla
Infratemporal fenestra
Quadrate bone
Quadratojugal bone
Mandible
Tooth fused to jaw
Dentary bone
Jugal bone

TUATARA

CHAMELEON SKELETON

Maxilla
Orbit
Naris
Bony crest
Mandible
Cervical vertebra
Sternum
Thoracolumbar vertebra
Phalanx
Humerus
Rib
Pubis
Ilium
Ischium
Ulna
Radius
Femur
Fibula
Phalanx
Tibia

Caudal vertebra

CHAMELEON

Phalanx
Tarsal
Tibia
Metatarsal
Knee joint
Fibula
Femur
Thoracolumbar vertebra
Ilium
Ischium
Neural spine
Sacrum
Transverse process
Femur
Tibia
Fibula
Tarsal
Caudal vertebra
Metatarsal
Phalanx

Bird skeletons

MOST BIRDS HAVE SKELETONS ADAPTED for flight. The majority of these adaptations serve to make the skeleton lighter; they include hollow bones strengthened with struts; the fusing of some bones, such as the tarsometatarsus; a lightweight, horny beak instead of a heavy jawbone and teeth; forelimbs modified to form wings; and a sternum (breastbone) enlarged to form a central keel to which the powerful flight muscles – the pectoralis and supracoracoideus – are attached. The backbone (vertebral column) is also relatively short to increase stability during flight. Birds have resilient legs that provide support, enable them to walk, push the body off the ground at take-off, and absorb most of the force of landing. The skeletons of flightless birds show adaptations for different types of movement. For example, the penguin is well adapted for aquatic life by having forelimbs and hind limbs modified for swimming under water.

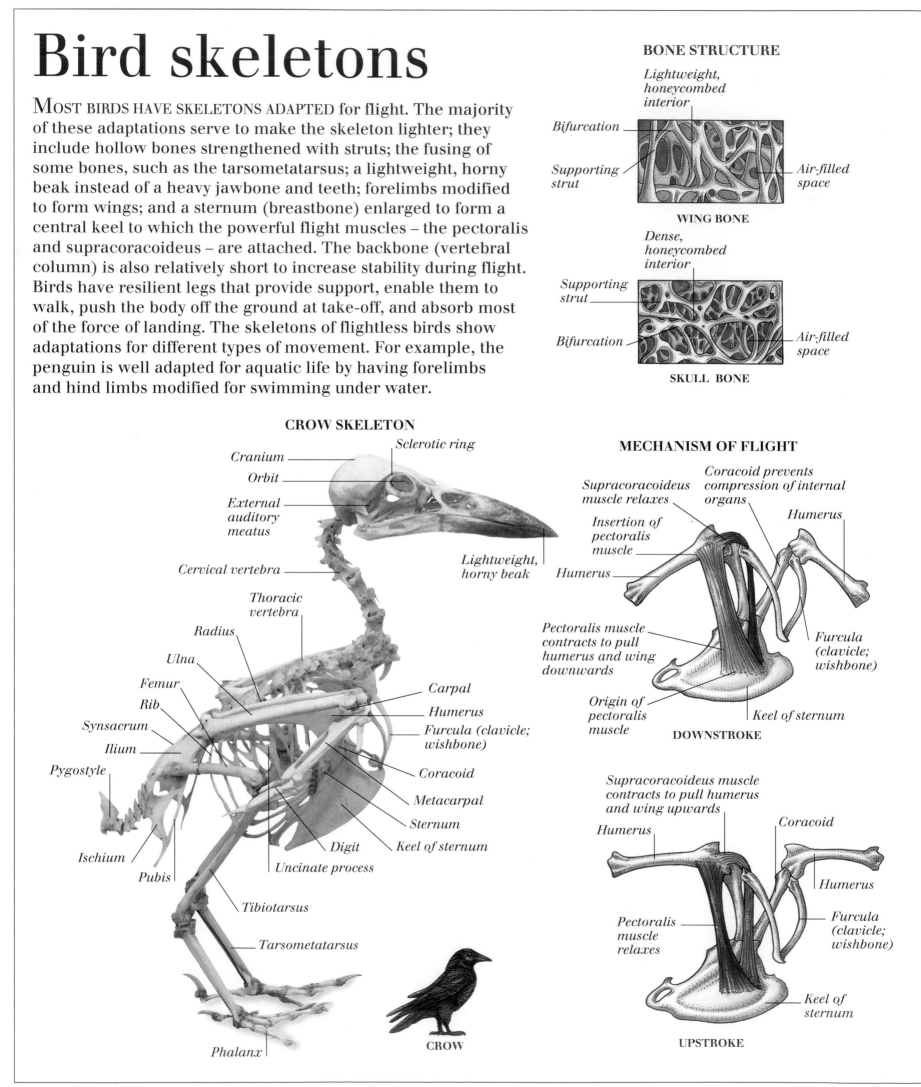

BONE STRUCTURE

Lightweight, honeycombed interior

Bifurcation

Supporting strut

Air-filled space

WING BONE

Dense, honeycombed interior

Supporting strut

Bifurcation

Air-filled space

SKULL BONE

CROW SKELETON

Cranium

Sclerotic ring

Orbit

External auditory meatus

Lightweight, horny beak

Cervical vertebra

Thoracic vertebra

Radius

Ulna

Femur

Rib

Synsacrum

Ilium

Pygostyle

Carpal

Humerus

Furcula (clavicle; wishbone)

Coracoid

Metacarpal

Sternum

Keel of sternum

Digit

Uncinate process

Ischium

Pubis

Tibiotarsus

Tarsometatarsus

Phalanx

CROW

MECHANISM OF FLIGHT

Supracoracoideus muscle relaxes

Coracoid prevents compression of internal organs

Humerus

Insertion of pectoralis muscle

Humerus

Pectoralis muscle contracts to pull humerus and wing downwards

Furcula (clavicle; wishbone)

Origin of pectoralis muscle

Keel of sternum

DOWNSTROKE

Supracoracoideus muscle contracts to pull humerus and wing upwards

Coracoid

Humerus

Humerus

Pectoralis muscle relaxes

Furcula (clavicle; wishbone)

Keel of sternum

UPSTROKE

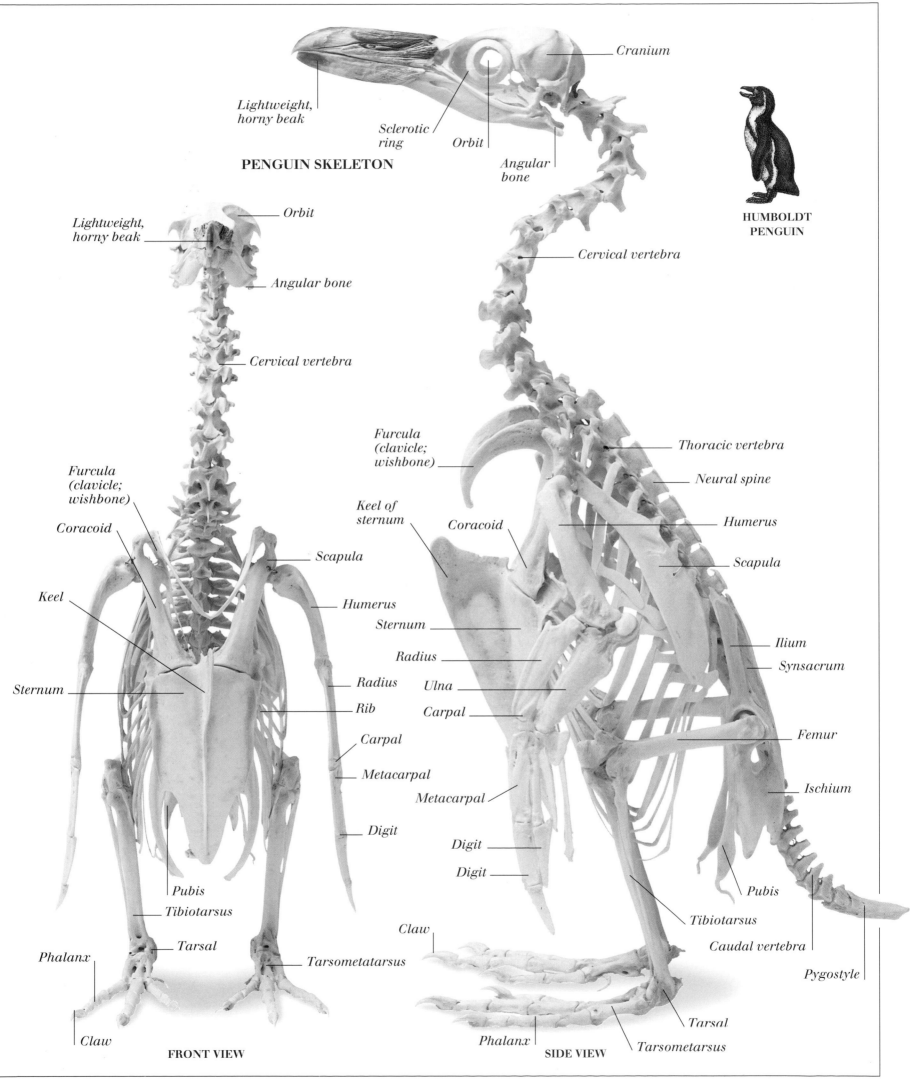

PENGUIN SKELETON

Lightweight, horny beak

Sclerotic ring

Orbit

Angular bone

Cranium

HUMBOLDT PENGUIN

Cervical vertebra

Lightweight, horny beak

Orbit

Angular bone

Cervical vertebra

Furcula (clavicle; wishbone)

Thoracic vertebra

Neural spine

Keel of sternum

Coracoid

Humerus

Coracoid

Scapula

Keel

Humerus

Scapula

Sternum

Sternum

Radius

Ilium

Radius

Synsacrum

Ulna

Rib

Carpal

Carpal

Metacarpal

Femur

Metacarpal

Digit

Ischium

Digit

Pubis

Digit

Tibiotarsus

Pubis

Tarsal

Tibiotarsus

Phalanx

Tarsometatarsus

Claw

Caudal vertebra

Pygostyle

Claw

Tarsal

Phalanx

SIDE VIEW

Tarsometatarsus

FRONT VIEW

Sea mammal skeletons

SEA MAMMALS INCLUDE ANIMALS that spend their life in water, such as whales and dolphins, and those that live mostly in water but come ashore to breed, such as seals, sea lions, and walruses. All evolved from land-living mammals, and their skeletons show numerous adaptations to aquatic life. Seal forelimbs and hind limbs are modified to form flippers, with short arm and leg bones and long phalanges (finger and toe bones). Earless seals use their front flippers for steering and their hind flippers for propulsion. In contrast, fur seals and sea lions use their front flippers for propulsion and their hind flippers for steering. The backbone of seals is highly flexible, allowing rapid turning in water and caterpillar-like shuffling movements on land. The whale skeleton produces a streamlined, fish-like shape, with an elongated head, a short neck, and a long, tapering body with no hind limbs. The forelimbs, which are used for steering, have shortened arm bones and extra phalanges (finger bones) to increase rigidity. Muscles attached above and below the whale's long, flexible backbone contract alternately to move the tail flukes up and down and produce forward thrust.

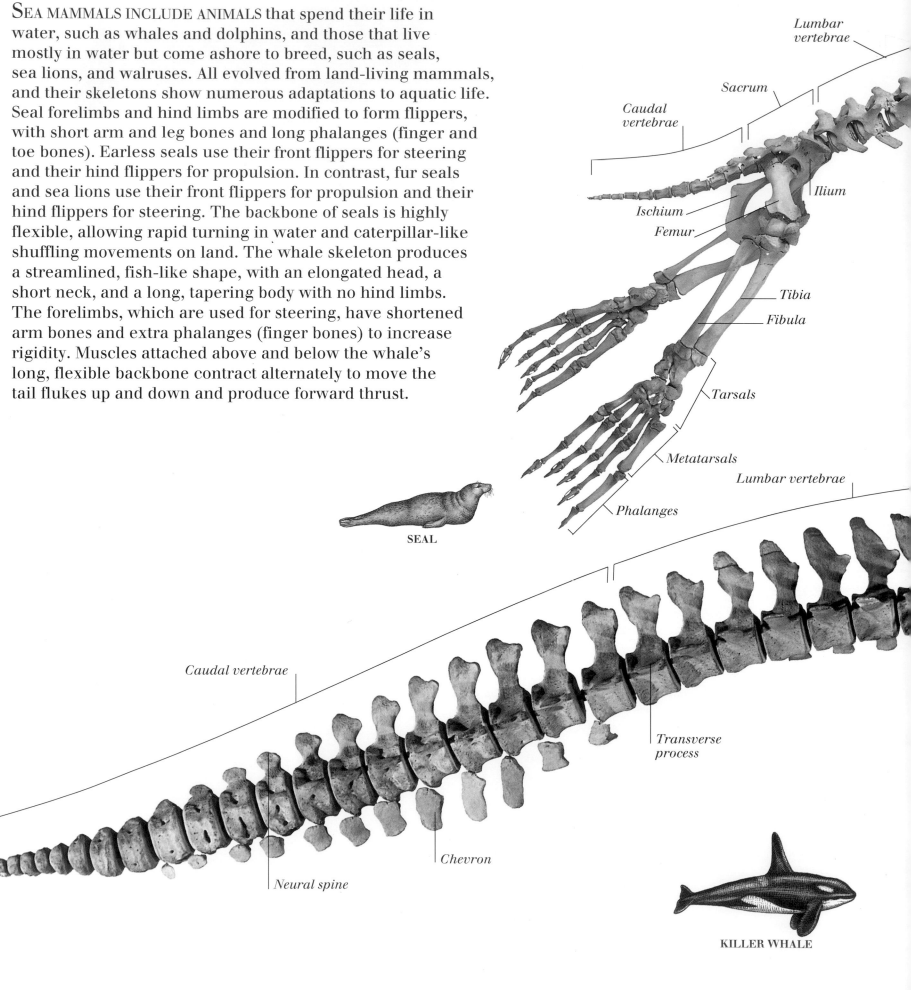

Lumbar vertebrae

Sacrum

Caudal vertebrae

Ischium

Femur

Ilium

Tibia

Fibula

Tarsals

Metatarsals

Lumbar vertebrae

Phalanges

SEAL

Caudal vertebrae

Transverse process

Chevron

Neural spine

KILLER WHALE

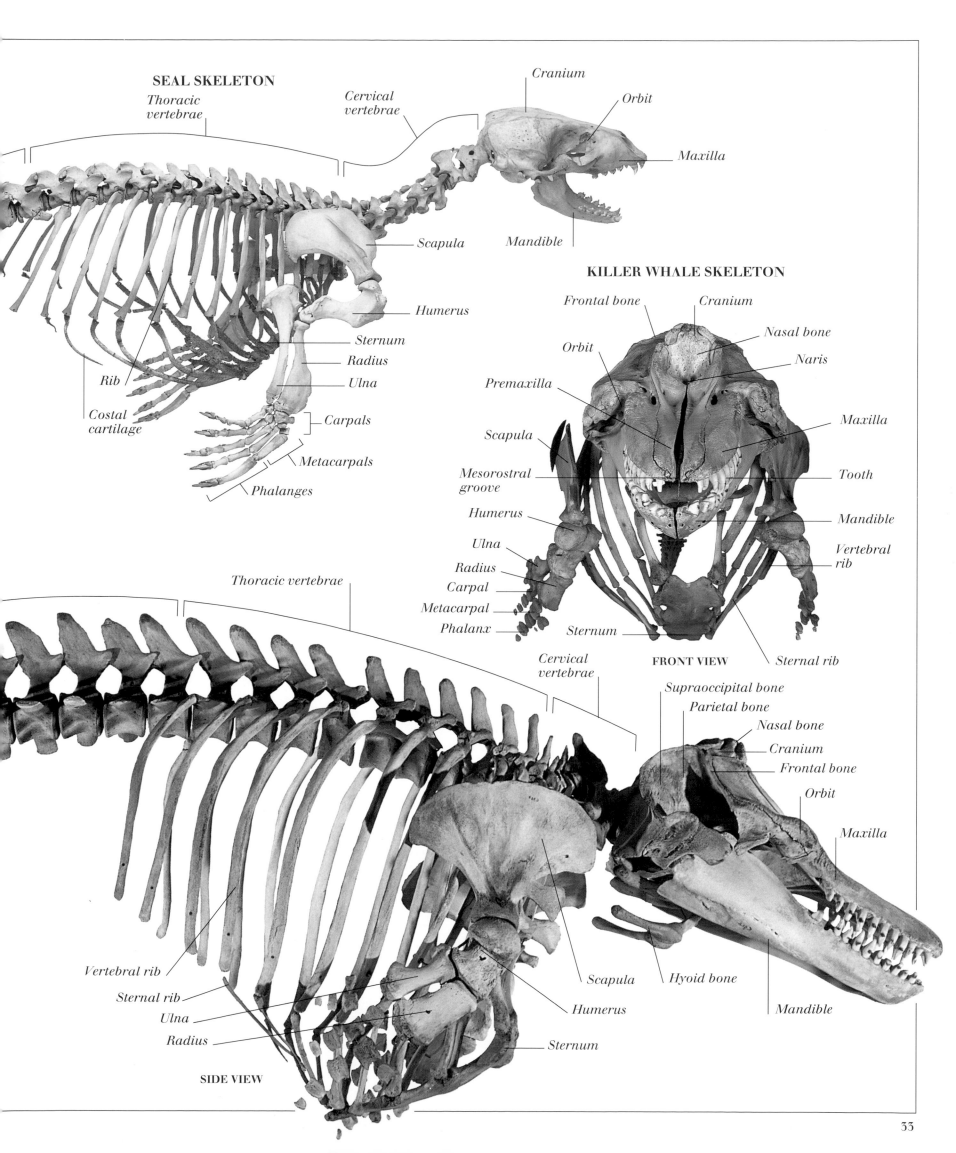

SEAL SKELETON

Thoracic vertebrae

Cervical vertebrae

Cranium

Orbit

Maxilla

Scapula

Mandible

Humerus

Sternum

Radius

Ulna

Rib

Carpals

Costal cartilage

Metacarpals

Phalanges

KILLER WHALE SKELETON

Frontal bone

Cranium

Nasal bone

Orbit

Naris

Premaxilla

Maxilla

Scapula

Mesorostral groove

Tooth

Humerus

Mandible

Ulna

Radius

Vertebral rib

Carpal

Metacarpal

Phalanx

Sternum

Sternal rib

FRONT VIEW

Thoracic vertebrae

Cervical vertebrae

Supraoccipital bone

Parietal bone

Nasal bone

Cranium

Frontal bone

Orbit

Maxilla

Vertebral rib

Sternal rib

Ulna

Radius

Scapula

Humerus

Hyoid bone

Sternum

Mandible

SIDE VIEW

33

Land mammal skeletons 1

LAND MAMMALS, unlike those that live in the sea, are not supported by the medium that surrounds them. Their entire weight is supported by the skeleton, in particular the strong backbone (vertebral column), and limbs that act as struts to hold the body off the ground. Mammals vary in the way the limbs support their body weight. In small, scampering mammals, such as squirrels and guinea pigs, the whole foot lies flat on the ground. Larger mammals typically raise the heel off the ground: cats and tigers walk on their toes; horses walk on one hoofed digit. The elephant has pillar-like limb bones to support its weight. However, not all land mammals fit into this pattern. For example, the platypus has short, broad limbs, but is adapted more for swimming than walking, whereas the bat's forelimbs are adapted for flight. The kangaroo hops on its hind limbs and uses its tail for balance and support.

BAT SKELETON

BAT

Skull
Carpal
Mandible
Clavicle
Sternum
Radius
Metacarpal
Ulna
Thoracic vertebra
Femur
Tarsal
Tibia
Metatarsal
Phalanx
Phalanx

PLATYPUS SKELETON

Premaxilla
Mandible
Maxilla
Cranium
Atlas
Orbit
Axis
Claw
Phalanx
Scapula
Metacarpal
Radius
Carpal
Ulna
Humerus
Rib
Costal enlargement of rib
Epipubic bone
Sacrum
Ilium
Femur
Ischium
Phalanx
Fibula
Metatarsal
Tibia
Tarsal
Patella

PLATYPUS

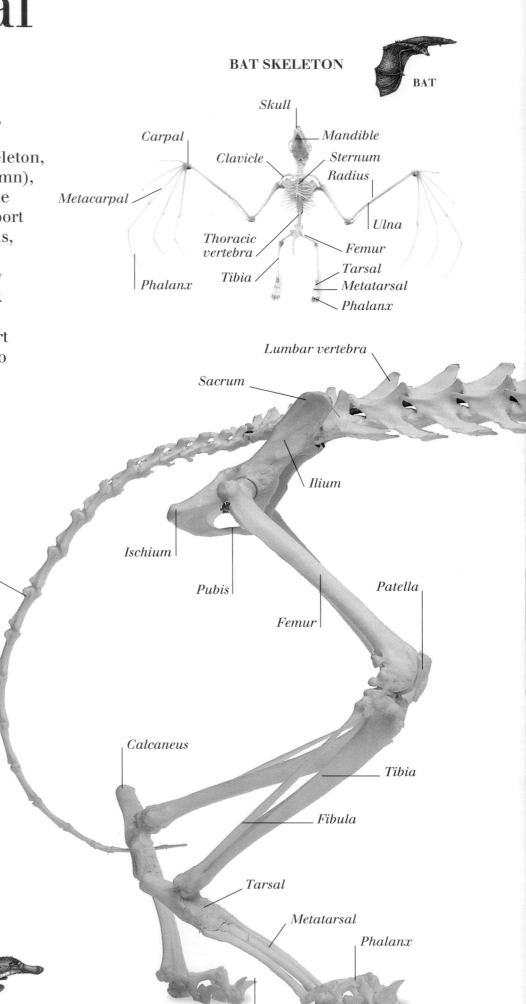

Lumbar vertebra
Sacrum
Ilium
Caudal vertebra
Ischium
Pubis
Patella
Femur
Calcaneus
Tibia
Fibula
Tarsal
Metatarsal
Phalanx
Retractable claw

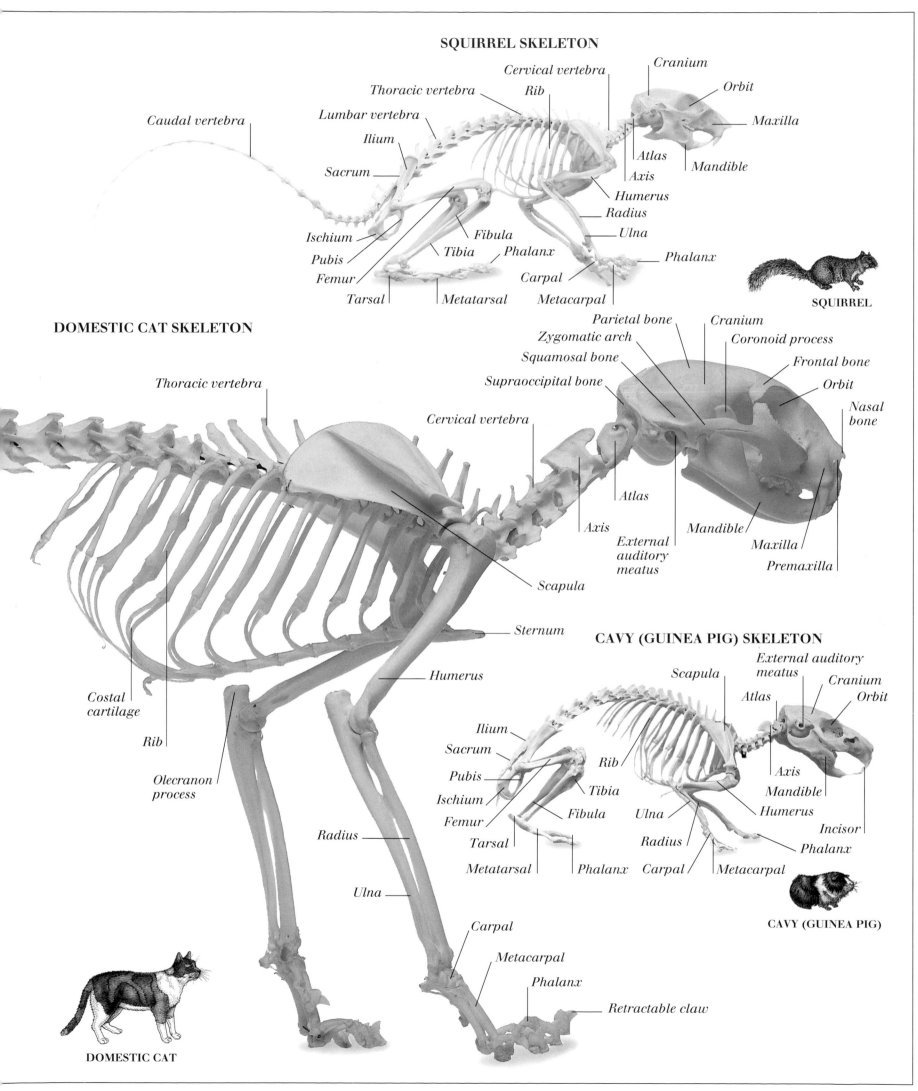

SQUIRREL SKELETON

Caudal vertebra

Thoracic vertebra
Lumbar vertebra
Ilium
Sacrum

Cervical vertebra
Rib

Cranium
Orbit
Maxilla

Atlas
Axis
Mandible

Humerus
Radius
Ulna

Ischium
Pubis
Femur

Fibula
Tibia

Phalanx
Carpal

Phalanx
Metacarpal

Tarsal
Metatarsal

SQUIRREL

DOMESTIC CAT SKELETON

Thoracic vertebra

Cervical vertebra

Parietal bone
Zygomatic arch
Squamosal bone
Supraoccipital bone

Cranium
Coronoid process
Frontal bone
Orbit
Nasal bone

Atlas
Axis
External auditory meatus

Mandible
Maxilla
Premaxilla

Scapula

Sternum

CAVY (GUINEA PIG) SKELETON

Costal cartilage
Rib

Humerus

Scapula
Ilium
Sacrum
Pubis
Ischium
Femur

External auditory meatus
Atlas
Cranium
Orbit

Rib
Tibia
Fibula

Axis
Mandible
Humerus

Incisor

Olecranon process

Tarsal
Metatarsal
Phalanx

Ulna
Radius
Carpal
Metacarpal

Phalanx

Radius

CAVY (GUINEA PIG)

Ulna

Carpal
Metacarpal
Phalanx
Retractable claw

DOMESTIC CAT

Land mammal skeletons 2

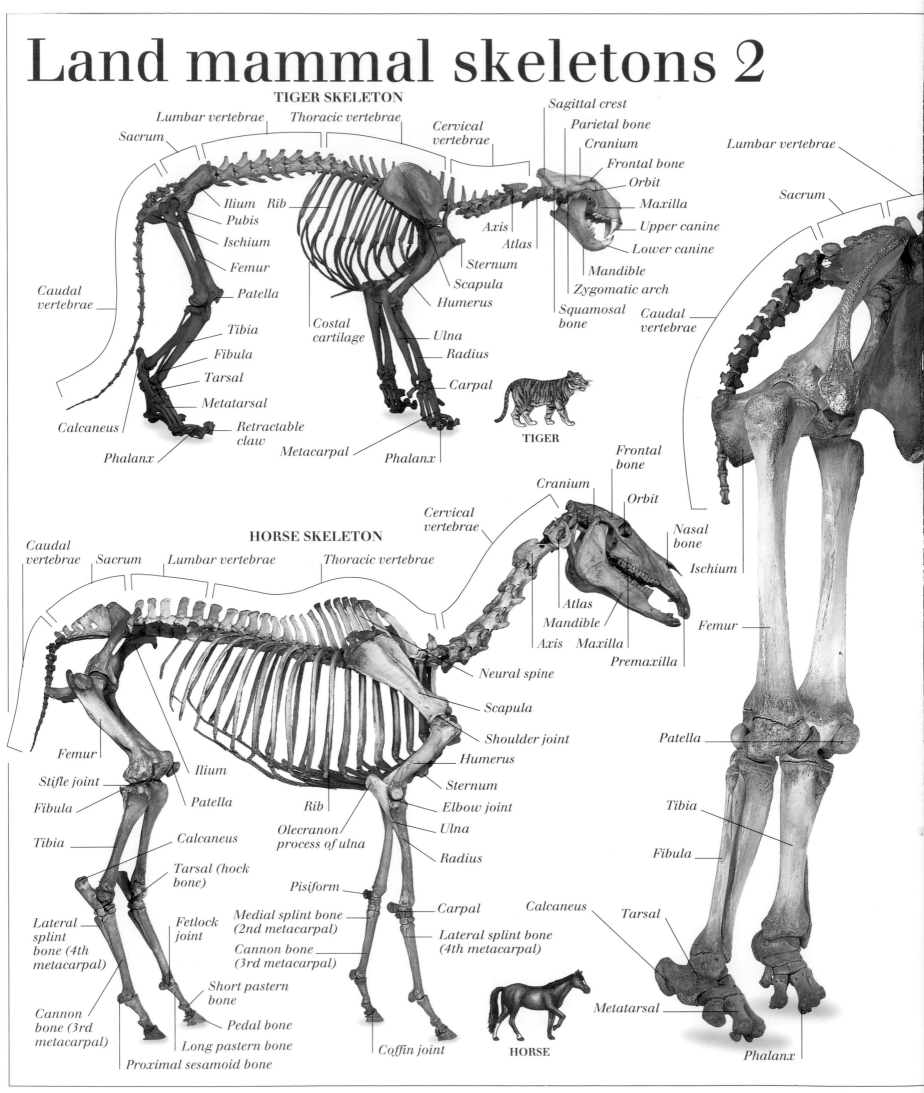

TIGER SKELETON

Lumbar vertebrae
Thoracic vertebrae
Cervical vertebrae
Sagittal crest
Parietal bone
Sacrum
Cranium
Lumbar vertebrae
Frontal bone
Orbit
Sacrum
Ilium
Rib
Maxilla
Pubis
Axis
Upper canine
Ischium
Atlas
Lower canine
Femur
Mandible
Sternum
Patella
Scapula
Zygomatic arch
Caudal vertebrae
Humerus
Squamosal bone
Caudal vertebrae
Tibia
Costal cartilage
Fibula
Ulna
Tarsal
Radius
Calcaneus
Carpal
Metatarsal
Retractable claw
Phalanx
Metacarpal
Phalanx

TIGER

Frontal bone

Cranium
Cervical vertebrae
Orbit
HORSE SKELETON
Nasal bone
Caudal vertebrae
Sacrum
Lumbar vertebrae
Thoracic vertebrae
Ischium
Atlas
Mandible
Femur
Axis
Maxilla
Premaxilla
Neural spine
Scapula
Femur
Shoulder joint
Stifle joint
Ilium
Humerus
Patella
Fibula
Patella
Sternum
Tibia
Tibia
Calcaneus
Rib
Elbow joint
Olecranon process of ulna
Ulna
Fibula
Pisiform
Radius
Lateral splint bone (4th metacarpal)
Tarsal (hock bone)
Calcaneus
Fetlock joint
Medial splint bone (2nd metacarpal)
Carpal
Tarsal
Lateral splint bone (4th metacarpal)
Cannon bone (3rd metacarpal)
Short pastern bone
Cannon bone (3rd metacarpal)
Pedal bone
Metatarsal
Long pastern bone
Coffin joint
HORSE
Phalanx
Proximal sesamoid bone

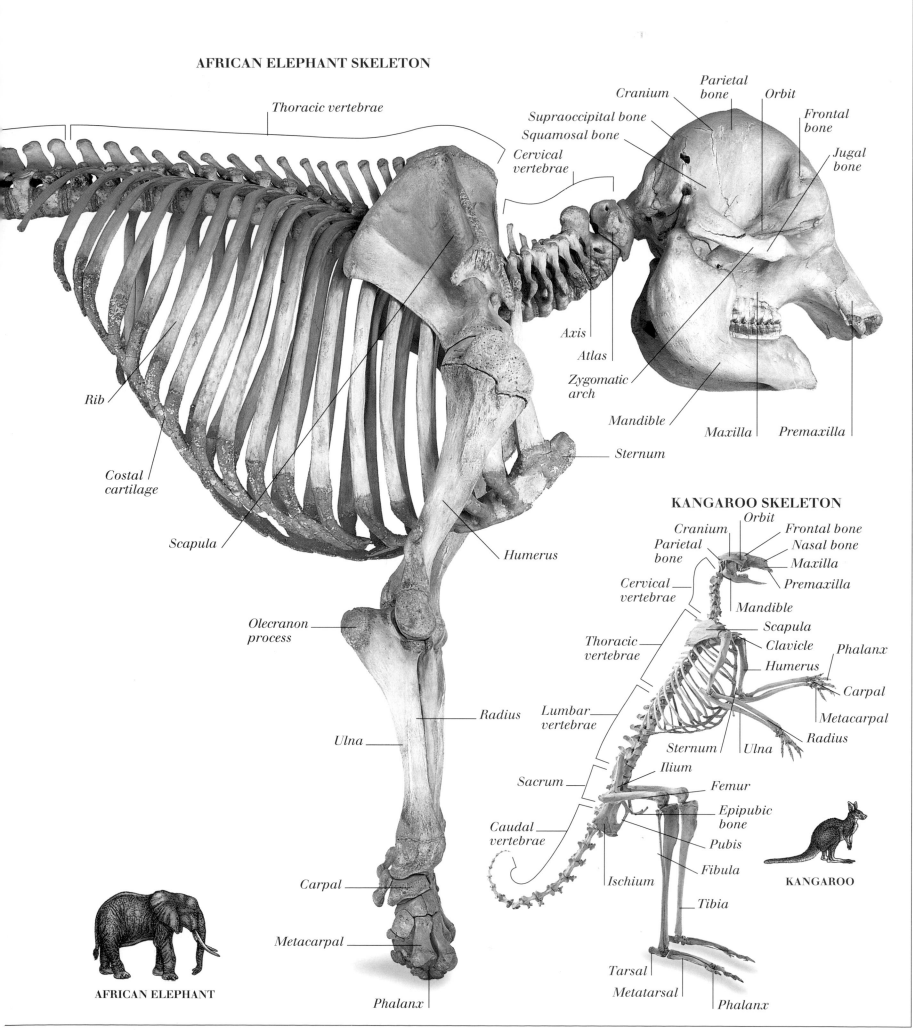

AFRICAN ELEPHANT SKELETON

Thoracic vertebrae

Parietal bone

Cranium

Orbit

Supraoccipital bone

Frontal bone

Squamosal bone

Jugal bone

Cervical vertebrae

Axis

Atlas

Zygomatic arch

Mandible

Maxilla

Premaxilla

Rib

Sternum

Costal cartilage

Scapula

Humerus

KANGAROO SKELETON

Orbit

Cranium

Frontal bone

Parietal bone

Nasal bone

Maxilla

Premaxilla

Cervical vertebrae

Mandible

Scapula

Olecranon process

Thoracic vertebrae

Clavicle

Humerus

Phalanx

Carpal

Metacarpal

Radius

Lumbar vertebrae

Ulna

Radius

Ulna

Sternum

Sacrum

Ilium

Femur

Epipubic bone

Caudal vertebrae

Pubis

Ischium

Fibula

KANGAROO

Tibia

Carpal

Tarsal

Metacarpal

Metatarsal

Phalanx

AFRICAN ELEPHANT

Phalanx

37

Early human relatives

THE DEVELOPMENT OF the modern human skeleton has involved changes associated with the shift from a quadrupedal (four-footed) stance to an upright, bipedal (two-footed) stance, and also with an enlarging cranium. Ape-like *Proconsul africanus*, which lived 20 million years ago, had the long pelvis and arms typical of a quadrupedal stance. However, hominid fossil remains from 5 million years ago have strong leg bones, a broad pelvis, and an S-shaped backbone, suggesting a bipedal stance. These features can be seen in 3-million-year-old *Australopithecus afarensis* ("Lucy"), and also in later skeletons, such as those of *Homo erectus* (Upright Man), *Homo neanderthalensis* (Neanderthal Man), and *Homo sapiens* (modern human). However, *Homo sapiens* has a larger brain than its ancestors, with a smaller face and jaw. All whole skeletons and external views shown here are reconstructions.

HOMO NEANDERTHALENSIS CRANIUM

AUSTRALOPITHECUS AFARENSIS ("LUCY")

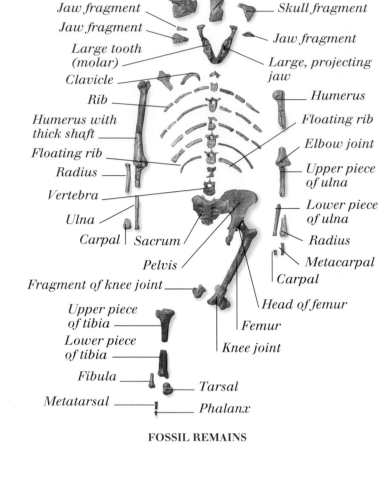

Skull fragment — Skull fragment
Jaw fragment — Skull fragment
Jaw fragment — Jaw fragment
Large tooth (molar) — Large, projecting jaw
Clavicle — Humerus
Rib — Floating rib
Humerus with thick shaft — Elbow joint
Floating rib — Upper piece of ulna
Radius — Lower piece of ulna
Vertebra — Radius
Ulna — Metacarpal
Carpal | Sacrum — Carpal
Pelvis — Head of femur
Fragment of knee joint — Femur
Upper piece of tibia — Knee joint
Lower piece of tibia
Fibula — Tarsal
Metatarsal — Phalanx

FOSSIL REMAINS

PROCONSUL AFRICANUS

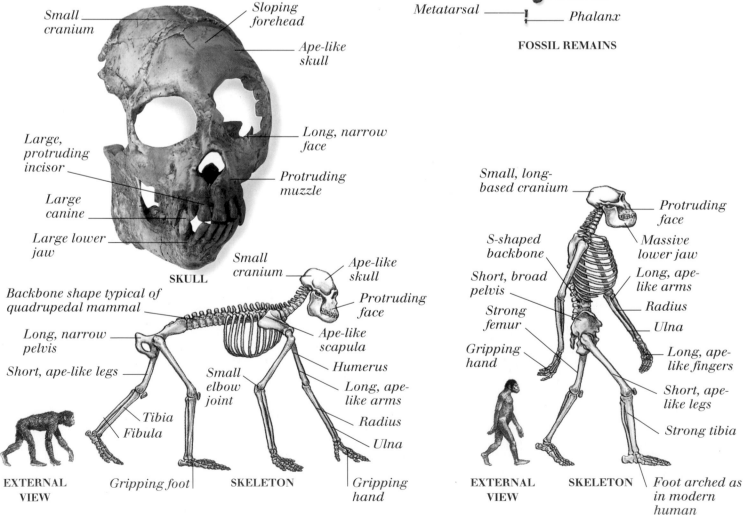

Small cranium — Sloping forehead
— Ape-like skull
Large, protruding incisor — Long, narrow face
Large canine — Protruding muzzle
Large lower jaw
SKULL

Small cranium — Ape-like skull
Backbone shape typical of quadrupedal mammal — Protruding face
Long, narrow pelvis — Ape-like scapula
Short, ape-like legs — Humerus
Small elbow joint — Long, ape-like arms
Tibia — Radius
Fibula — Ulna
EXTERNAL VIEW Gripping foot **SKELETON** Gripping hand

Small, long-based cranium — Protruding face
S-shaped backbone — Massive lower jaw
Short, broad pelvis — Long, ape-like arms
Strong femur — Radius
Gripping hand — Ulna
— Long, ape-like fingers
— Short, ape-like legs
— Strong tibia
EXTERNAL VIEW **SKELETON** Foot arched as in modern human

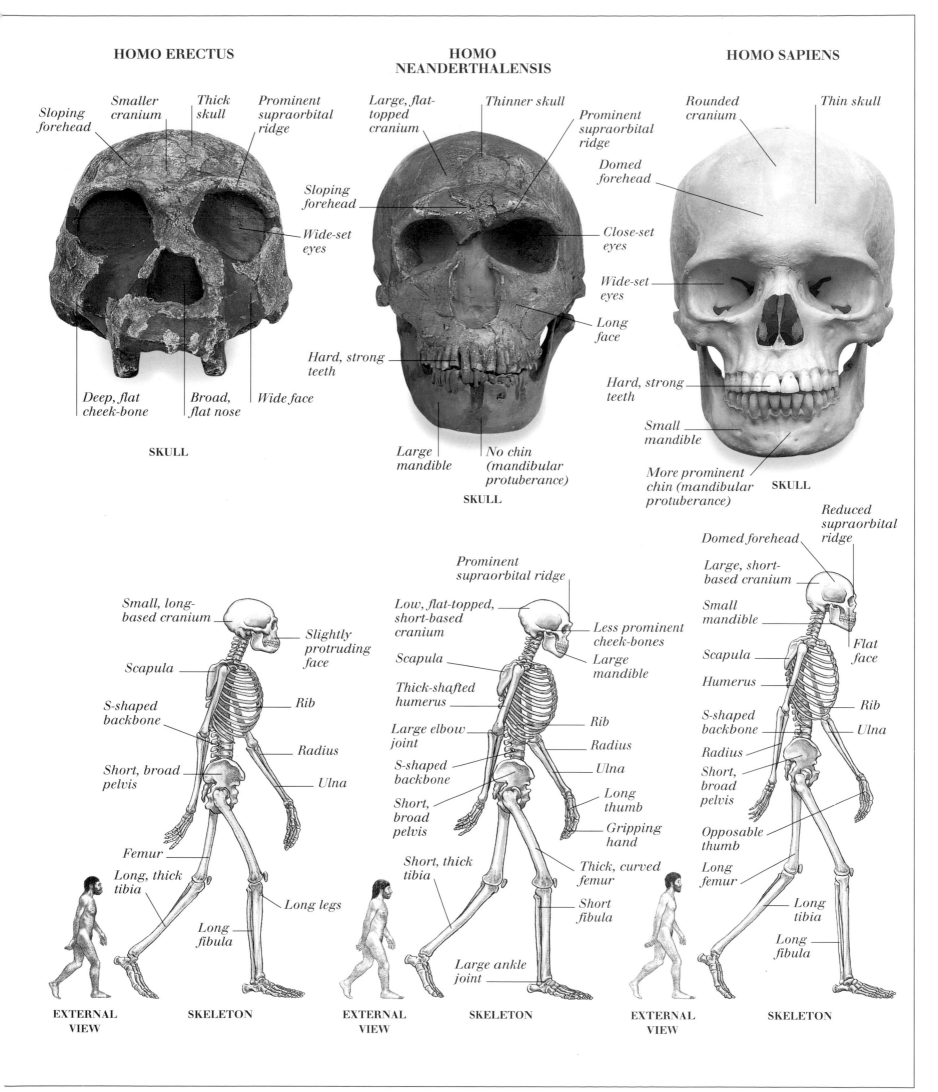

HOMO ERECTUS

SKULL

Sloping forehead
Smaller cranium
Thick skull
Prominent supraorbital ridge
Wide-set eyes
Deep, flat cheek-bone
Broad, flat nose
Wide face

HOMO NEANDERTHALENSIS

SKULL

Large, flat-topped cranium
Thinner skull
Prominent supraorbital ridge
Sloping forehead
Close-set eyes
Long face
Hard, strong teeth
Large mandible
No chin (mandibular protuberance)

HOMO SAPIENS

SKULL

Rounded cranium
Thin skull
Domed forehead
Wide-set eyes
Hard, strong teeth
Small mandible
More prominent chin (mandibular protuberance)

HOMO ERECTUS (Skeleton)

Small, long-based cranium
Slightly protruding face
Scapula
Rib
S-shaped backbone
Radius
Short, broad pelvis
Ulna
Femur
Long, thick tibia
Long legs
Long fibula

EXTERNAL VIEW **SKELETON**

HOMO NEANDERTHALENSIS (Skeleton)

Prominent supraorbital ridge
Low, flat-topped, short-based cranium
Less prominent cheek-bones
Scapula
Large mandible
Thick-shafted humerus
Rib
Large elbow joint
Radius
S-shaped backbone
Ulna
Short, broad pelvis
Long thumb
Gripping hand
Short, thick tibia
Thick, curved femur
Short fibula
Large ankle joint

EXTERNAL VIEW **SKELETON**

HOMO SAPIENS (Skeleton)

Reduced supraorbital ridge
Domed forehead
Large, short-based cranium
Small mandible
Scapula
Flat face
Humerus
Rib
S-shaped backbone
Ulna
Radius
Short, broad pelvis
Opposable thumb
Long femur
Long tibia
Long fibula

EXTERNAL VIEW **SKELETON**

Bone structure and function

LIVING BONE IS A HARD, constantly changing, self-repairing tissue that is supplied with blood vessels and nerves. It consists of bone cells and the intercellular matrix that lies between them. About 65 per cent of this matrix consists of mineral salts, mainly calcium phosphate, that give bone its hardness; the other 35 per cent consists mainly of collagen fibres that provide flexibility. Bones have a thin outer coat of periosteum which contains osteoblasts (bone-forming cells) and osteoclasts (bone-destroying cells). Within the periosteum is a layer of compact bone that consists of concentric cylinders (lamellae) of matrix called osteons (Haversian systems) each of which acts as a weight-bearing pillar. Osteons are laid down around a central (Haversian) canal, which contains the blood vessels that supply osteocytes (mature bone cells) with nutrients and oxygen; Volkmann's canals connect adjacent Haversian canals. Bone matrix is maintained by osteocytes, which are found in lacunae (chambers) at the junctions of lamellae. Osteocytes communicate through dendrites (cell processes) that pass along tiny canals known as canaliculi. Spongy (cancellous) bone is situated within compact bone and consists of struts (trabeculae) that make it both light and strong. Red bone marrow, found in the spaces within cancellous bone, produces red and white blood cells.

MICROGRAPH OF LAMELLA FRAGMENT

Bone matrix

Layers of collagen fibres and mineral salts

Lamella (layer of bone)

Crystallites aligned parallel to collagen fibres

MICROGRAPH OF SPONGY BONE

Trabecula (strut)

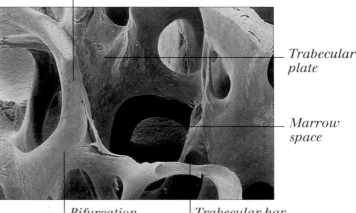

Trabecular plate

Marrow space

Bifurcation

Trabecular bar

MICROGRAPH OF OSTEON

STRUCTURAL FEATURES OF BONE

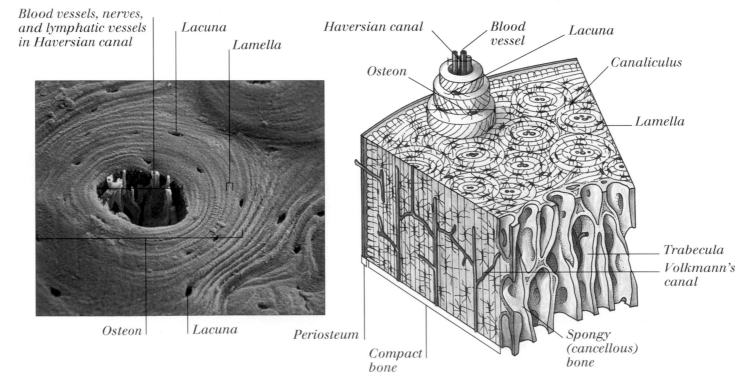

Blood vessels, nerves, and lymphatic vessels in Haversian canal

Lacuna

Lamella

Osteon

Lacuna

Osteon

Lacuna

Periosteum

Haversian canal

Blood vessel

Lacuna

Canaliculus

Lamella

Compact bone

Trabecula

Volkmann's canal

Spongy (cancellous) bone

MICROGRAPH OF OSTEOCYTE IN LACUNA

Canaliculus *Lacuna* *Bone matrix*

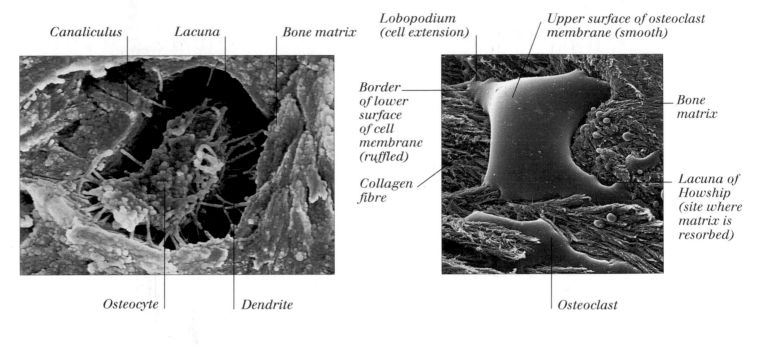

Osteocyte *Dendrite*

MICROGRAPH OF OSTEOCLAST

Lobopodium (cell extension) *Upper surface of osteoclast membrane (smooth)*

Border of lower surface of cell membrane (ruffled)

Collagen fibre

Bone matrix

Lacuna of Howship (site where matrix is resorbed)

Osteoclast

MICROGRAPH OF RED BONE MARROW

Lymphocyte *Monocyte* *Neutrophil*

Basophilic normoblast

Polychromatic normoblast

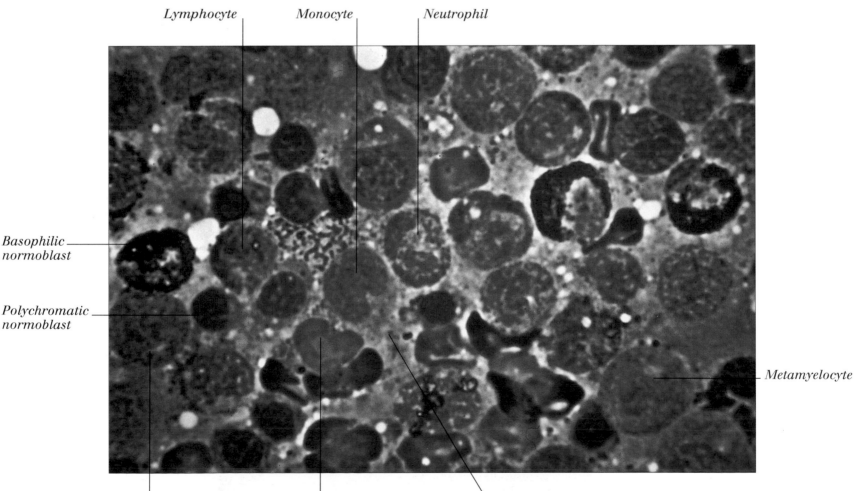

Metamyelocyte

Eosinophil *Erythrocyte* *Mass of platelets*

Joints

A JOINT IS A SITE where two or more bones meet. Joints have two main functions: to allow movement, and to maintain stability. Tough, inelastic ligaments prevent joint dislocation. There are three types of joints: immobile fibrous joints, such as the sutures between skull bones; slightly movable cartilaginous joints, such as those between vertebrae; and highly mobile synovial joints. Most body joints are synovial. To enable smooth movement, the ends of the bones of synovial joints are covered with glassy hyaline cartilage and separated by a cavity filled with synovial fluid. Five main types of synovial joints are found in mammals: pivot joints permit rotation of one bone against or inside another; ball-and-socket joints allow movement in all directions; hinge joints allow bending and straightening only; saddle joints permit backwards, forwards, and side-to-side movements; and plane joints allow short, gliding movements.

SUTURES OF SKULL

HIP JOINT LIGAMENTS

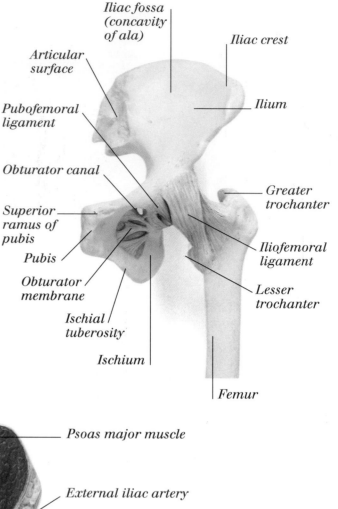

Iliac fossa (concavity of ala)
Iliac crest
Articular surface
Ilium
Pubofemoral ligament
Obturator canal
Greater trochanter
Superior ramus of pubis
Pubis
Iliofemoral ligament
Obturator membrane
Lesser trochanter
Ischial tuberosity
Ischium
Femur

ANATOMY OF HIP JOINT

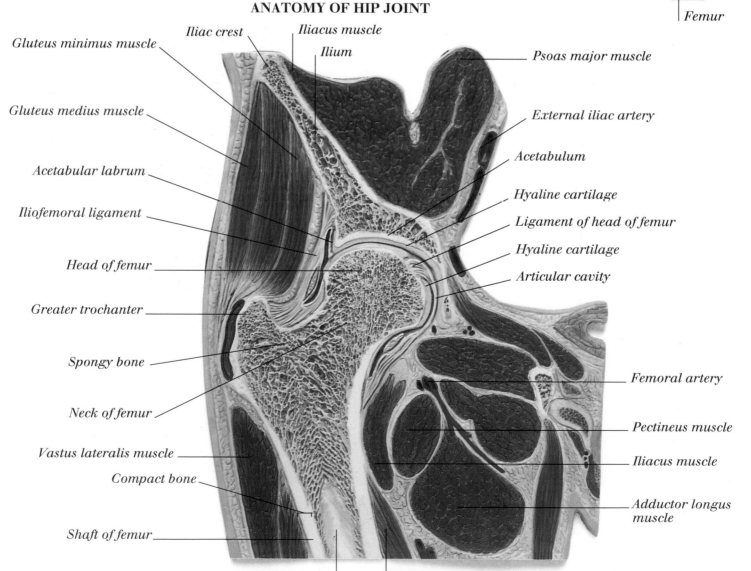

Gluteus minimus muscle
Iliac crest
Iliacus muscle
Ilium
Psoas major muscle
Gluteus medius muscle
External iliac artery
Acetabular labrum
Acetabulum
Hyaline cartilage
Iliofemoral ligament
Ligament of head of femur
Hyaline cartilage
Head of femur
Articular cavity
Greater trochanter
Spongy bone
Femoral artery
Neck of femur
Pectineus muscle
Vastus lateralis muscle
Iliacus muscle
Compact bone
Adductor longus muscle
Shaft of femur
Bone marrow cavity
Vastus medialis muscle

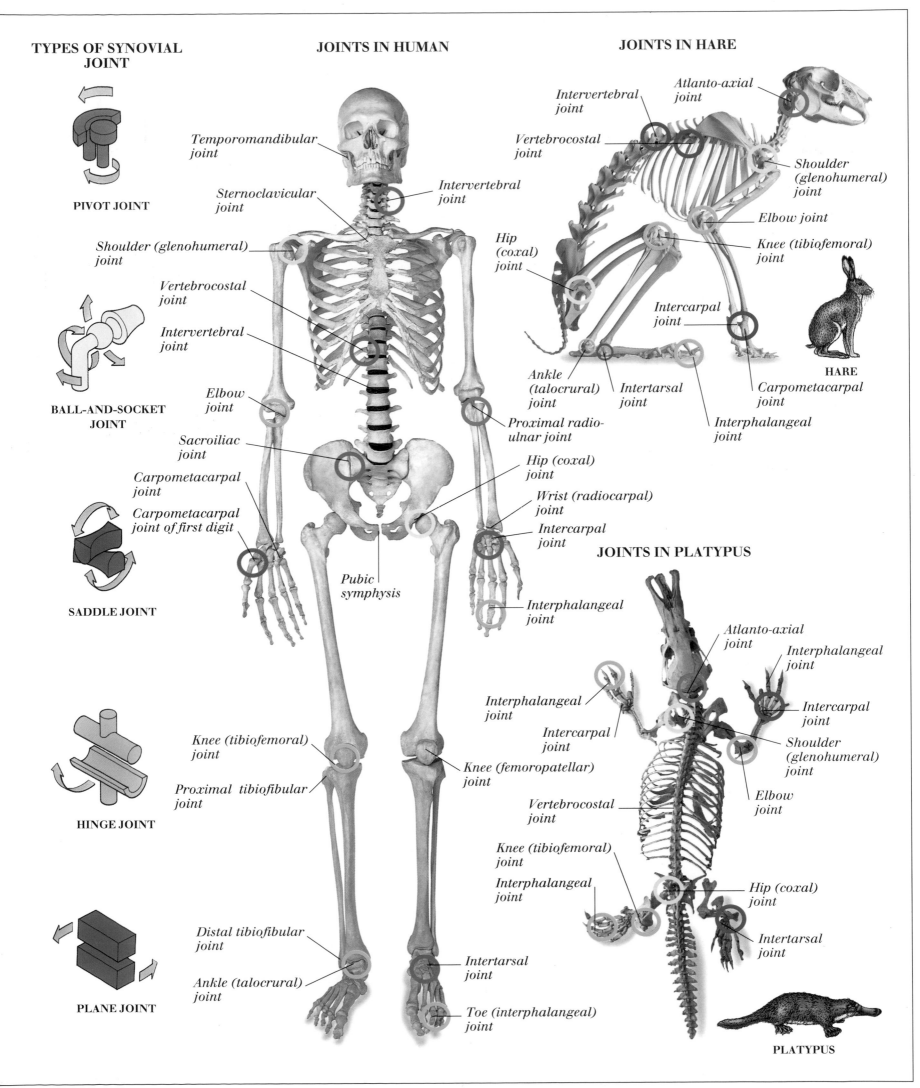

TYPES OF SYNOVIAL JOINT

PIVOT JOINT

BALL-AND-SOCKET JOINT

SADDLE JOINT

HINGE JOINT

PLANE JOINT

JOINTS IN HUMAN

Temporomandibular joint

Sternoclavicular joint

Intervertebral joint

Shoulder (glenohumeral) joint

Vertebrocostal joint

Intervertebral joint

Elbow joint

Sacroiliac joint

Carpometacarpal joint

Carpometacarpal joint of first digit

Pubic symphysis

Proximal radio-ulnar joint

Hip (coxal) joint

Wrist (radiocarpal) joint

Intercarpal joint

Interphalangeal joint

Knee (tibiofemoral) joint

Proximal tibiofibular joint

Knee (femoropatellar) joint

Distal tibiofibular joint

Ankle (talocrural) joint

Intertarsal joint

Toe (interphalangeal) joint

JOINTS IN HARE

Intervertebral joint

Atlanto-axial joint

Vertebrocostal joint

Shoulder (glenohumeral) joint

Hip (coxal) joint

Elbow joint

Knee (tibiofemoral) joint

Intercarpal joint

Ankle (talocrural) joint

Intertarsal joint

Carpometacarpal joint

Interphalangeal joint

HARE

JOINTS IN PLATYPUS

Atlanto-axial joint

Interphalangeal joint

Interphalangeal joint

Intercarpal joint

Intercarpal joint

Shoulder (glenohumeral) joint

Elbow joint

Vertebrocostal joint

Knee (tibiofemoral) joint

Interphalangeal joint

Hip (coxal) joint

Intertarsal joint

PLATYPUS

43

Human skulls

THE BONES OF THE HUMAN SKULL serve several functions: the cranial bones surround and protect the brain, while the facial bones provide attachment points for facial muscles, as well as openings for eating and breathing, and cavities for the sensory organs. The facial bones also provide anchorage for the teeth. With the exception of the mandible (lower jaw) and the ear ossicles, the skull bones are knitted together by immovable joints called sutures. To allow blood vessels, nerves, and the spinal cord to pass through the skull, the skull bones are perforated by foramina (holes). The bone structure of early human skulls differs greatly from that of modern humans. The 200,000-year-old specimen of a *Homo heidelbergensis* skull (originally called "Rhodesian Man") has no forehead, prominent supraorbital (brow) ridges, and a large upper jaw. The skull of *Homo neanderthalensis* ("Neanderthal Man") – who lived 100,000 to 35,000 years ago and immediately preceded *Homo sapiens* (modern human) in Europe – had heavy supraorbital ridges and a sharply sloping forehead. In contrast, the skull of *Homo sapiens* has a more domed forehead, a flatter face, and a smaller jaw.

HOMO HEIDELBERGENSIS ("RHODESIAN MAN")

EXTERNAL VIEW

Prominent supraorbital ridge

Frontal bone

Parietal bone

Ethmoid bone

Orbit

Nasal bone

Sphenoid bone

Maxilla

Zygomatic bone

Zygomatic arch

Occipital bone

External auditory meatus

Temporal bone

SKULL

HOMO NEANDERTHALENSIS

Parietal bone

EXTERNAL VIEW

Frontal bone

Prominent supraorbital ridge

Ethmoid bone

Orbit

Lacrimal bone

Protruding nose

Sphenoid bone

Zygomatic bone

Maxilla

Occipital bone

Zygomatic arch

Small mastoid process

Temporal bone

SKULL

External auditory meatus

HOMO SAPIENS SKULL

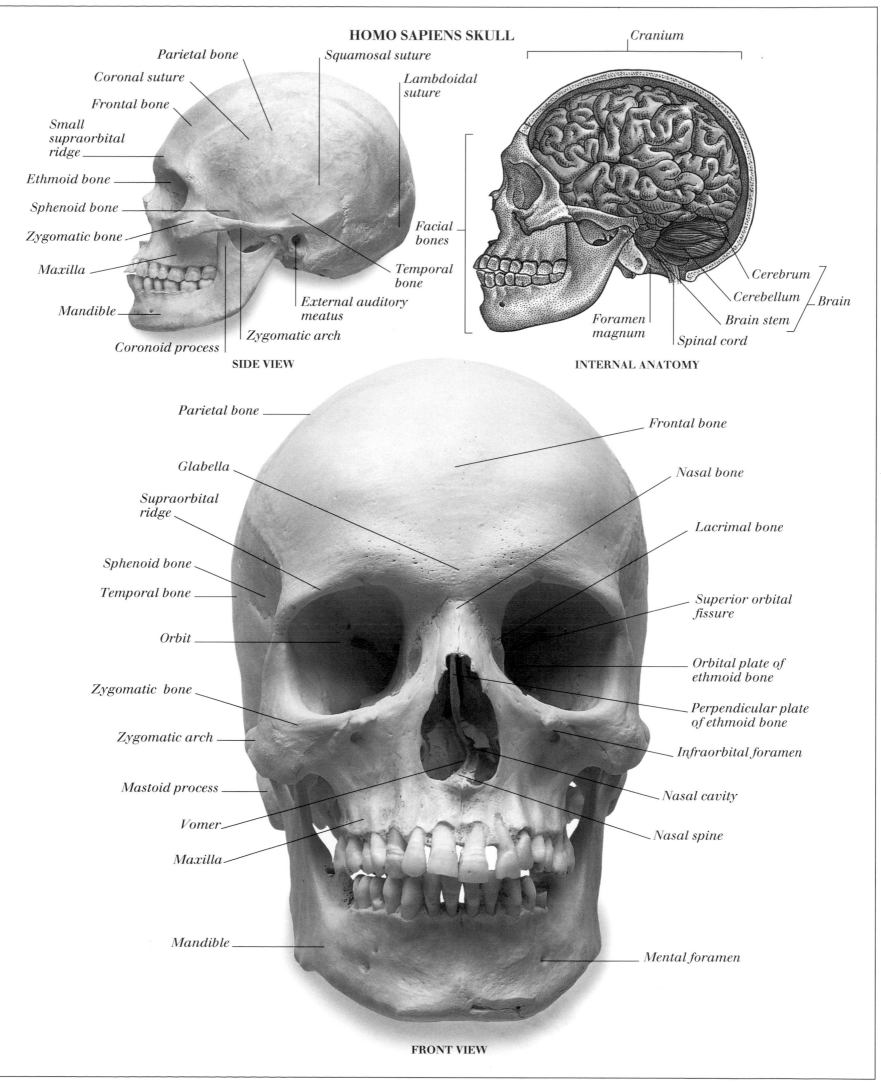

SIDE VIEW

Parietal bone
Coronal suture
Frontal bone
Small supraorbital ridge
Ethmoid bone
Sphenoid bone
Zygomatic bone
Maxilla
Mandible
Coronoid process
Zygomatic arch
External auditory meatus
Temporal bone
Squamosal suture
Lambdoidal suture
Facial bones

INTERNAL ANATOMY

Cranium
Cerebrum
Cerebellum
Brain stem
Brain
Spinal cord
Foramen magnum

FRONT VIEW

Parietal bone
Glabella
Supraorbital ridge
Sphenoid bone
Temporal bone
Orbit
Zygomatic bone
Zygomatic arch
Mastoid process
Vomer
Maxilla
Mandible
Frontal bone
Nasal bone
Lacrimal bone
Superior orbital fissure
Orbital plate of ethmoid bone
Perpendicular plate of ethmoid bone
Infraorbital foramen
Nasal cavity
Nasal spine
Mental foramen

45

Animal skulls

ALL VERTEBRATES HAVE A skull made of fused bones and a movable mandible (lower jaw). The function of the skull is to house and protect the brain and sensory organs, and to allow eating and breathing. Each species of animal has a skull shape adapted to its particular lifestyle. Typically, birds, such as vultures, have lightweight skulls; carnivores (meat eaters), such as lions and crocodiles, have powerful jaws with sharp teeth; the toothless anteater has a long snout that enables it to probe into ant nests for food; and herbivores (plant eaters), such as the goat, have a loose-fitting lower jaw that permits side-to-side movement for grinding food. The two main muscles involved in biting and chewing are the temporalis and the masseter. In carnivores, both these muscles move the lower jaw up and down with a scissor-like action. In herbivores, the temporalis is relatively weak and the masseter provides the force needed to grind tough vegetation.

KING VULTURE SKULL

Frontal bone
Postorbital bone
Pterygoid bone
Cranium
Orbit
Parietal bone
Ethmoid bone
Nasal bone
Maxilla
Premaxilla
Jugal bone
Dentary bone
Sharp beak for tearing
Supraoccipital bone
Angular bone
Quadrate bone

KING VULTURE

BORDER COLLIE SKULL

Frontal bone
Cranium
Orbit
Lacrimal bone
Parietal bone
Maxilla
Nasal bone
Premaxilla
Squamosal bone
External auditory meatus
Zygomatic arch
Jugal bone
Mandible
Mental foramen
Canine
Incisor

BORDER COLLIE

LION SKULL

Frontal bone
Coronoid process
Orbit
Jugal bone
Sagittal crest
Parietal bone
Cranium
Maxilla
Nasal bone
Premaxilla
Upper canine
Supraoccipital bone
Squamosal bone
External auditory meatus
Mandibular condyle
Zygomatic arch
Carnassial tooth
Lower canine
Mandible

LION

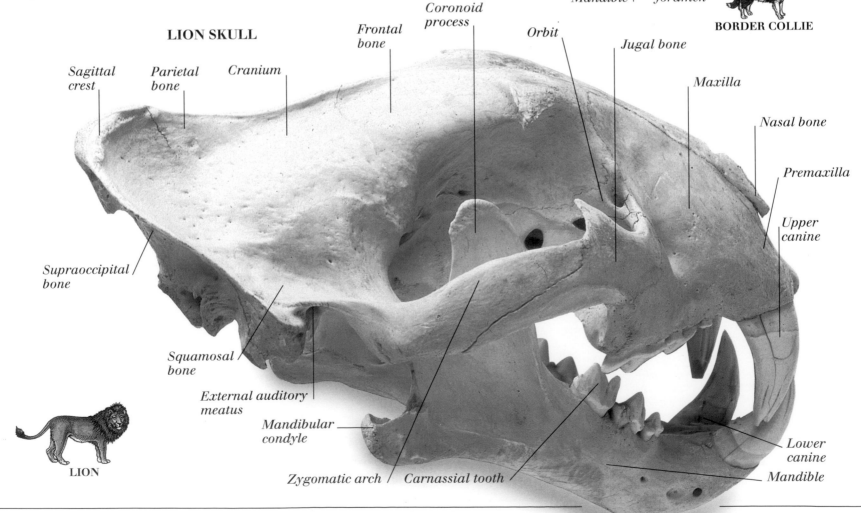

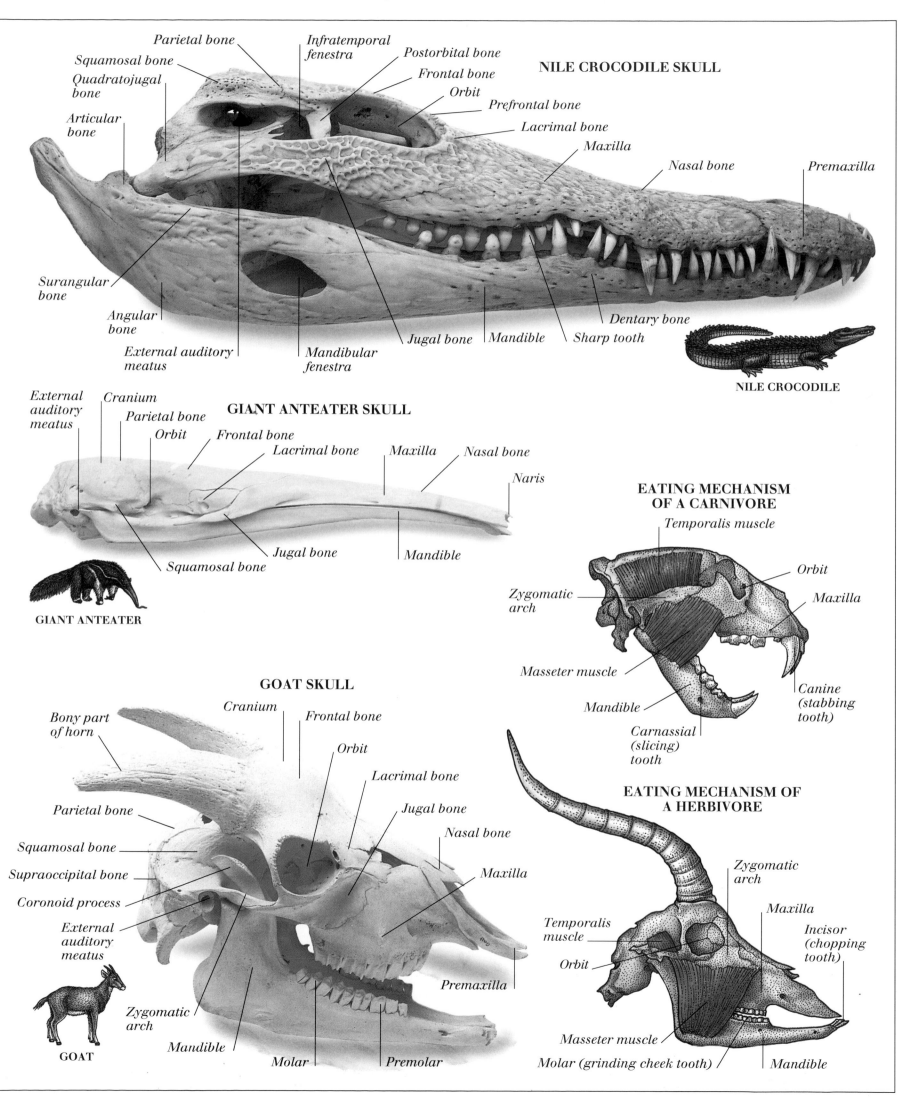

NILE CROCODILE SKULL

Parietal bone
Squamosal bone
Quadratojugal bone
Articular bone
Infratemporal fenestra
Postorbital bone
Frontal bone
Orbit
Prefrontal bone
Lacrimal bone
Maxilla
Nasal bone
Premaxilla
Surangular bone
Angular bone
External auditory meatus
Mandibular fenestra
Jugal bone
Mandible
Dentary bone
Sharp tooth

NILE CROCODILE

GIANT ANTEATER SKULL

External auditory meatus
Cranium
Parietal bone
Orbit
Frontal bone
Lacrimal bone
Maxilla
Nasal bone
Naris
Jugal bone
Mandible
Squamosal bone

GIANT ANTEATER

EATING MECHANISM OF A CARNIVORE

Temporalis muscle
Orbit
Maxilla
Zygomatic arch
Masseter muscle
Mandible
Canine (stabbing tooth)
Carnassial (slicing) tooth

GOAT SKULL

Cranium
Frontal bone
Orbit
Lacrimal bone
Jugal bone
Nasal bone
Maxilla
Bony part of horn
Parietal bone
Squamosal bone
Supraoccipital bone
Coronoid process
External auditory meatus
Zygomatic arch
Mandible
Molar
Premolar
Premaxilla

GOAT

EATING MECHANISM OF A HERBIVORE

Temporalis muscle
Orbit
Zygomatic arch
Maxilla
Incisor (chopping tooth)
Masseter muscle
Molar (grinding cheek tooth)
Mandible

47

Backbone

ALL VERTEBRATES HAVE A BACKBONE (vertebral column), which acts like a girder carrying the weight of the organs of the body. The backbone consists of a row of vertebrae separated by cartilaginous intervertebral discs that give limited flexibility. These vertebrae also form a protective tunnel around the spinal cord, while the neural spine and transverse processes of the vertebrae provide attachment points for muscles and ligaments. There are five types of vertebrae: cervical (neck), thoracic (chest), lumbar (abdominal), sacral (anchoring the backbone to the pelvis), and caudal (tail). Unlike most other vertebrates, birds have inflexible backbones – although the neck is flexible – to provide stability in flight. Most mammalian backbones (such as the hare's) curve upwards to help resist the downward pull of body weight, and vertebrae increase in size towards the lumbar end where stress is greatest. The human backbone is adapted to supporting the body in an upright position: it has an S-shaped curve that serves to position the body directly over the legs and feet.

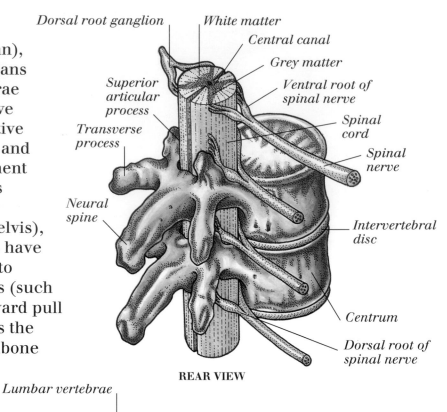

Dorsal root ganglion
White matter
Central canal
Grey matter
Superior articular process
Ventral root of spinal nerve
Transverse process
Spinal cord
Spinal nerve
Neural spine
Intervertebral disc
Centrum
Dorsal root of spinal nerve

REAR VIEW

Lumbar vertebrae

Sacrum

Coccyx

Inferior articular process
Superior articular process
Centrum

COMPONENTS OF HUMAN BACKBONE

Apex of sacrum
Transverse line (site of vertebral fusion)
Ala (lateral mass)
Coccygeal vertebrae (normally fused to form coccyx)
Superior articular process
Centrum of 1st sacral vertebra
Lumbosacral joint
Rudimentary transverse process
Sacral promontory
Coccygeal cornua
Facet for articulation with sacrum
Ventral sacral foramen
Pelvic sacral foramen

Pedicle of vertebral arch
Transverse process
Superior articular process
Superior articular facet
Lamina of vertebral arch
Neural spine
Centrum
Vertebral foramen
Transverse process

FRONT VIEW OF SACRUM AND COCCYGEAL VERTEBRAE

TOP VIEW OF LUMBAR VERTEBRA

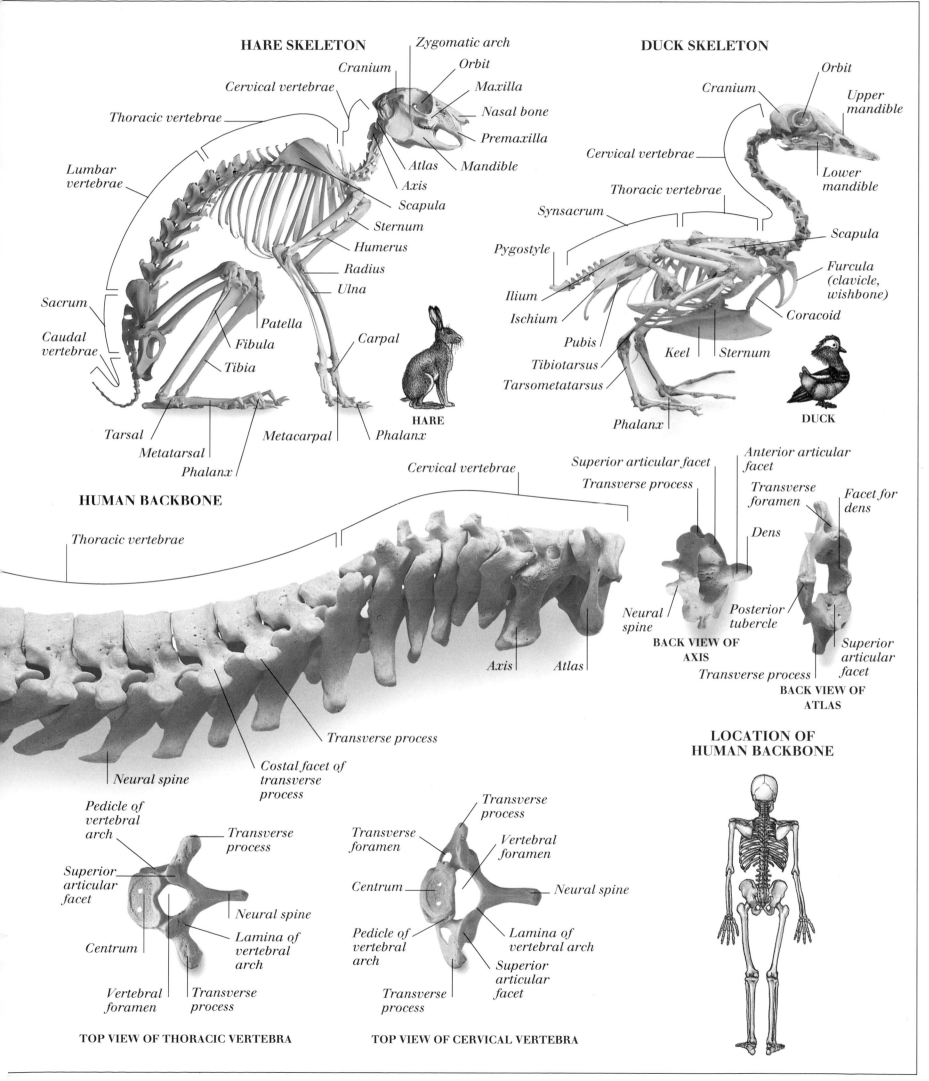

HARE SKELETON

Zygomatic arch
Cranium
Orbit
Cervical vertebrae
Maxilla
Thoracic vertebrae
Nasal bone
Premaxilla
Lumbar vertebrae
Atlas
Mandible
Axis
Scapula
Sternum
Humerus
Radius
Ulna
Sacrum
Caudal vertebrae
Patella
Fibula
Carpal
Tibia
Tarsal
Metatarsal
Phalanx
Metacarpal
Phalanx

HARE

DUCK SKELETON

Orbit
Cranium
Upper mandible
Cervical vertebrae
Lower mandible
Thoracic vertebrae
Scapula
Synsacrum
Pygostyle
Furcula (clavicle, wishbone)
Ilium
Coracoid
Ischium
Pubis
Keel
Sternum
Tibiotarsus
Tarsometatarsus
Phalanx

DUCK

HUMAN BACKBONE

Thoracic vertebrae
Cervical vertebrae
Superior articular facet
Transverse process
Anterior articular facet
Transverse foramen
Facet for dens
Dens
Neural spine
Posterior tubercle
Superior articular facet
Axis
Atlas

BACK VIEW OF AXIS

Transverse process
BACK VIEW OF ATLAS

Transverse process
Costal facet of transverse process
Neural spine

LOCATION OF HUMAN BACKBONE

Pedicle of vertebral arch
Transverse process
Transverse process
Superior articular facet
Transverse foramen
Vertebral foramen
Neural spine
Centrum
Centrum
Neural spine
Lamina of vertebral arch
Pedicle of vertebral arch
Lamina of vertebral arch
Vertebral foramen
Transverse process
Superior articular facet
Transverse process

TOP VIEW OF THORACIC VERTEBRA

TOP VIEW OF CERVICAL VERTEBRA

49

Ribcage

Ribs are curved, flattened bones found in all vertebrates.
In land vertebrates, the ribs typically articulate with the thoracic
vertebrae at one end and with the sternum (breastbone) at the
other to form the ribcage. The ribcage protects the heart and lungs
and is also flexible, allowing the lungs to inflate and deflate during
breathing. Limbless vertebrates, such as snakes, have a tubular
ribcage that supports the body and plays a part in locomotion.
Humans have twelve pairs of ribs. Ribs 1–7, the true ribs,
are attached to the sternum by costal cartilages. Ribs 8–12 are
called the false ribs: ribs 8–10 are connected to one another by
costal cartilage; ribs 11 and 12, the floating ribs, are connected
only to the vertebral column. Breathing involves the action of the
intercostal muscles (muscles between the ribs), and the diaphragm
(the muscle sheet that separates the chest from the abdomen).
When a person breathes in, the external intercostal muscles
contract, moving the ribcage upwards and outwards, and
the diaphragm contracts and flattens, drawing air into
the lungs. When the person breathes out, the process
is reversed, pushing air out of the lungs.

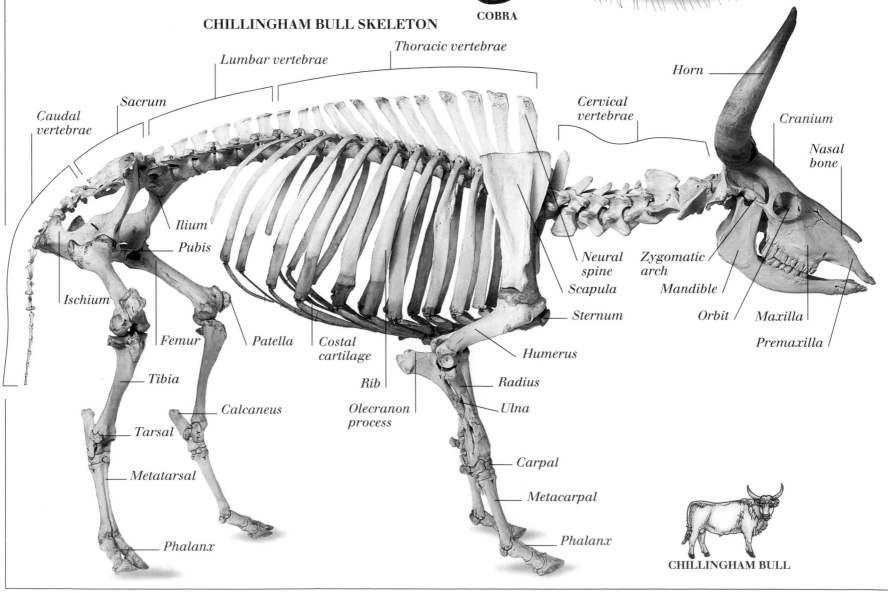

COBRA SKELETON

Cranium

Maxilla

Mandible

Vertebra

Rib

Articulation
between rib
and vertebra

Caudal
vertebra

COBRA

CHILLINGHAM BULL SKELETON

Thoracic vertebrae

Lumbar vertebrae

Cervical
vertebrae

Horn

Cranium

Sacrum

Nasal
bone

Caudal
vertebrae

Ilium

Pubis

Neural
spine

Zygomatic
arch

Scapula

Mandible

Ischium

Sternum

Orbit

Maxilla

Premaxilla

Femur

Patella

Costal
cartilage

Humerus

Tibia

Rib

Radius

Calcaneus

Olecranon
process

Ulna

Tarsal

Carpal

Metatarsal

Metacarpal

Phalanx

Phalanx

CHILLINGHAM BULL

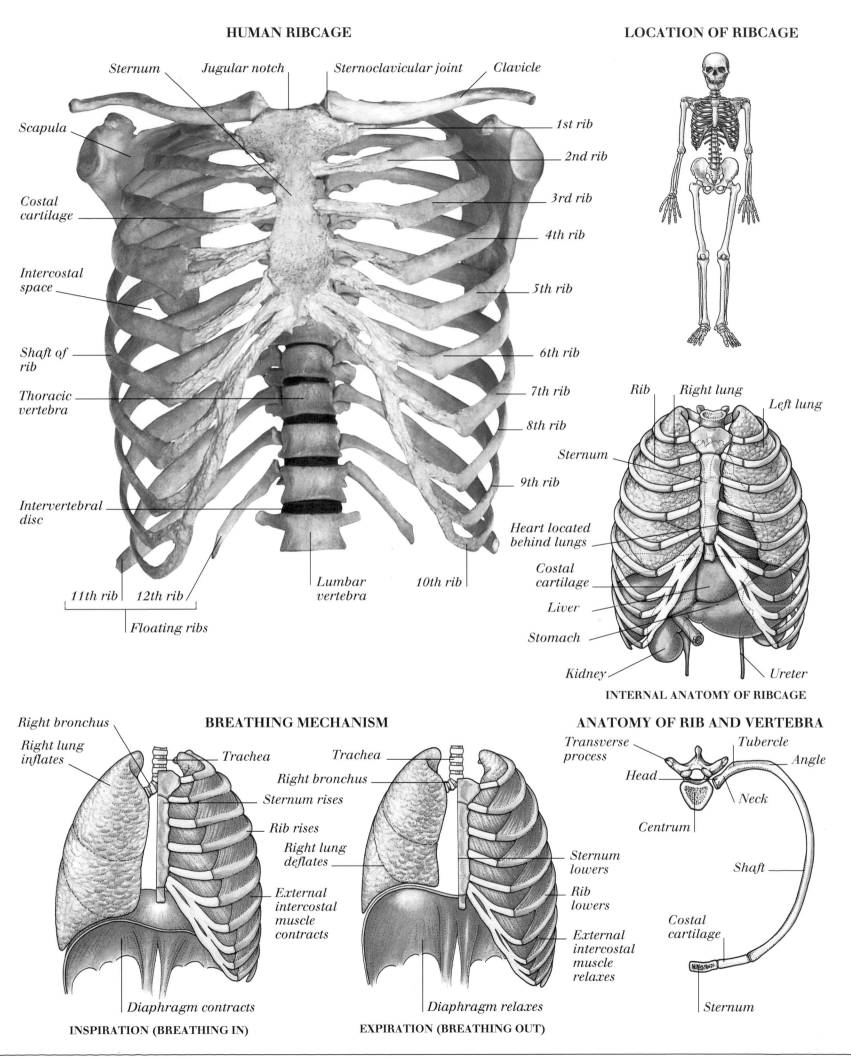

HUMAN RIBCAGE

Sternum
Jugular notch
Sternoclavicular joint
Clavicle

Scapula

Costal
cartilage

Intercostal
space

Shaft of
rib

Thoracic
vertebra

Intervertebral
disc

1st rib
2nd rib
3rd rib
4th rib
5th rib
6th rib
7th rib
8th rib
9th rib
10th rib

11th rib   12th rib

Floating ribs

Lumbar
vertebra

LOCATION OF RIBCAGE

Rib   Right lung
Left lung

Sternum

Heart located
behind lungs

Costal
cartilage

Liver

Stomach

Kidney
Ureter

INTERNAL ANATOMY OF RIBCAGE

BREATHING MECHANISM

Right bronchus
Right lung
inflates

Trachea

Trachea
Right bronchus
Sternum rises
Rib rises
Right lung
deflates
External
intercostal
muscle
contracts

Sternum
lowers
Rib
lowers
External
intercostal
muscle
relaxes

Diaphragm contracts

INSPIRATION (BREATHING IN)

Diaphragm relaxes

EXPIRATION (BREATHING OUT)

ANATOMY OF RIB AND VERTEBRA

Transverse
process

Tubercle
Angle

Head
Neck

Centrum

Shaft

Costal
cartilage

Sternum

Pelvis

THE PELVIS CONSISTS OF TWO COXAE (known as the pelvic girdle), the sacrum, and the coccyx. Together, these bones connect the hind limbs to the backbone, transmit the force from the hind limbs to the rest of the body, and support and protect the organs of the lower abdomen. Each coxa is formed by the fusion of three bones: the ilium, ischium, and pubis. The coxae are joined at a cartilaginous joint known as the pubic symphysis. The joints between the coxae and the sacrum are called the sacroiliac joints. Four-legged animals, such as dogs and cattle, typically have a horizontally aligned, elongated pelvis. Chimpanzees, with their semi-upright posture, have an elongated, slightly tilted pelvis. In humans, who are fully upright, the pelvis is rounded and nearly vertical, so that the body is balanced directly over the feet.

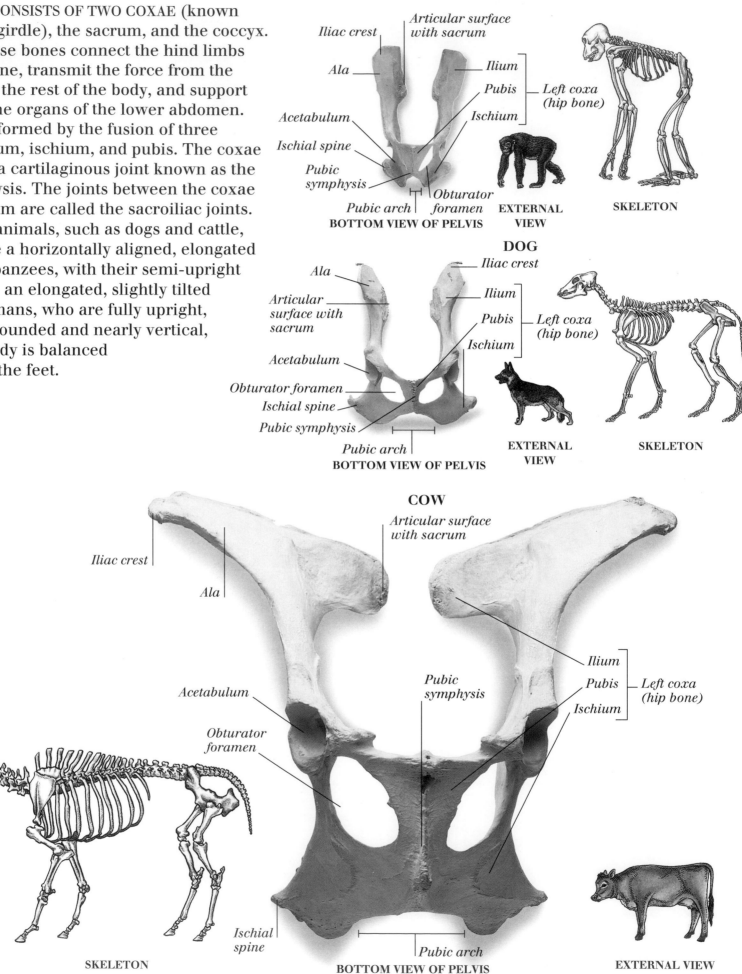

CHIMPANZEE

Iliac crest

Articular surface with sacrum

Ala

Ilium

Pubis

Left coxa (hip bone)

Acetabulum

Ischium

Ischial spine

Pubic symphysis

Obturator foramen

Pubic arch

BOTTOM VIEW OF PELVIS

EXTERNAL VIEW

SKELETON

DOG

Ala

Iliac crest

Articular surface with sacrum

Ilium

Pubis

Left coxa (hip bone)

Ischium

Acetabulum

Obturator foramen

Ischial spine

Pubic symphysis

Pubic arch

BOTTOM VIEW OF PELVIS

EXTERNAL VIEW

SKELETON

COW

Articular surface with sacrum

Iliac crest

Ala

Ilium

Pubic symphysis

Pubis

Left coxa (hip bone)

Acetabulum

Ischium

Obturator foramen

Ischial spine

Pubic arch

SKELETON

BOTTOM VIEW OF PELVIS

EXTERNAL VIEW

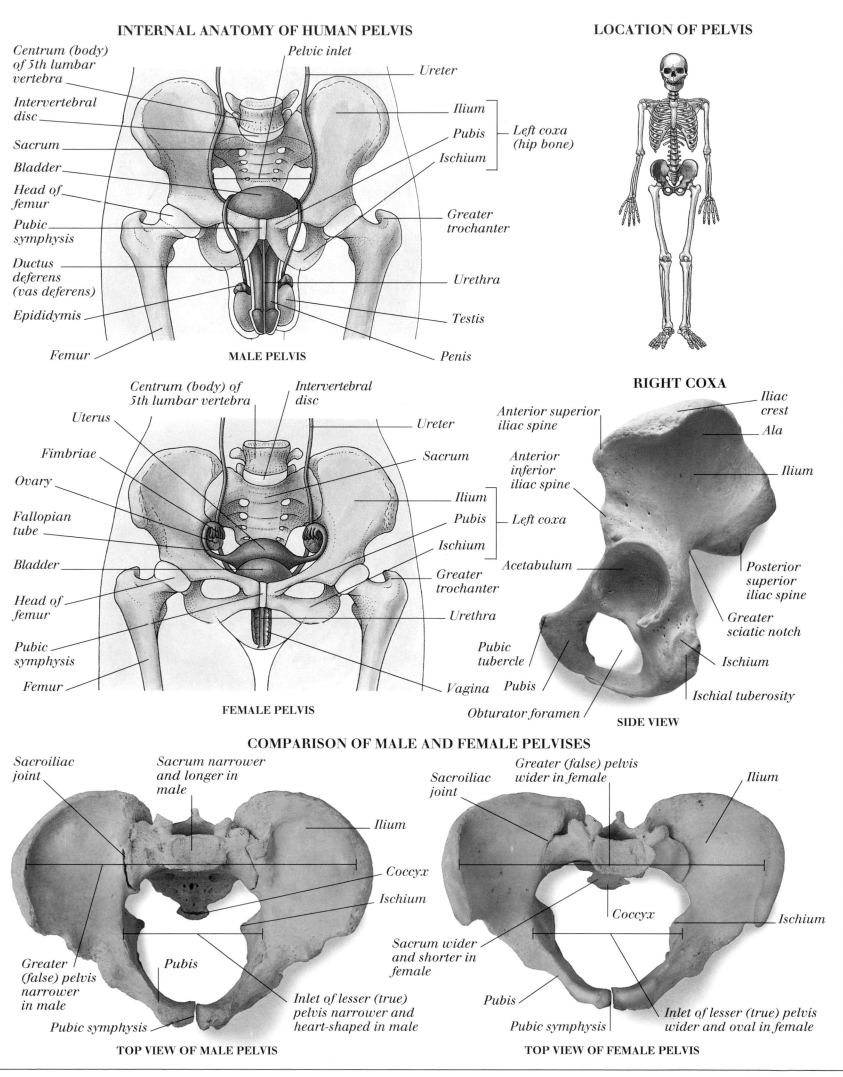

INTERNAL ANATOMY OF HUMAN PELVIS

Centrum (body) of 5th lumbar vertebra
Intervertebral disc
Sacrum
Bladder
Head of femur
Pubic symphysis
Ductus deferens (vas deferens)
Epididymis
Femur

Pelvic inlet

Ureter
Ilium
Pubis — Left coxa (hip bone)
Ischium
Greater trochanter
Urethra
Testis
Penis

MALE PELVIS

LOCATION OF PELVIS

Uterus
Fimbriae
Ovary
Fallopian tube
Bladder
Head of femur
Pubic symphysis
Femur

Centrum (body) of 5th lumbar vertebra
Intervertebral disc
Ureter
Sacrum
Ilium
Pubis — Left coxa
Ischium
Greater trochanter
Urethra
Vagina

FEMALE PELVIS

RIGHT COXA

Anterior superior iliac spine
Anterior inferior iliac spine
Acetabulum
Pubic tubercle
Pubis
Obturator foramen

Iliac crest
Ala
Ilium
Posterior superior iliac spine
Greater sciatic notch
Ischium
Ischial tuberosity

SIDE VIEW

COMPARISON OF MALE AND FEMALE PELVISES

Sacroiliac joint
Sacrum narrower and longer in male
Ilium
Coccyx
Ischium
Greater (false) pelvis narrower in male
Pubis
Pubic symphysis
Inlet of lesser (true) pelvis narrower and heart-shaped in male

TOP VIEW OF MALE PELVIS

Greater (false) pelvis wider in female
Sacroiliac joint
Ilium
Coccyx
Sacrum wider and shorter in female
Ischium
Pubis
Pubic symphysis
Inlet of lesser (true) pelvis wider and oval in female

TOP VIEW OF FEMALE PELVIS

Forelimbs

THE FORELIMBS OF TETRAPODS (four-limbed vertebrates) are typically used for support, movement, and varying degrees of manipulation. They originated from an ancestral pentadactyl (five-fingered) forelimb. This would have consisted of a humerus (upper arm bone); an ulna and radius (lower arm bones); ten carpals (wrist bones); five metacarpals (palm bones); and five sets of phalanges (finger bones). During evolution, the number, shape, and size of the forelimb bones changed to adapt vertebrates to particular lifestyles. For example, the short, strong forelimbs of the armadillo are adapted for digging; the arm and finger bones of the sea lion form a broad flipper for swimming; the gibbon's long arm bones and elongated, gripping fingers provide a secure hold on branches; and in flying vertebrates, such as the rock dove and bat, the forelimbs have become wings. Some fast-moving mammals – for example, horses and ponies – stand on a hoofed third digit; this is an adaptation for speed. The human forelimb is adapted mainly for intricate manipulation rather than support or locomotion.

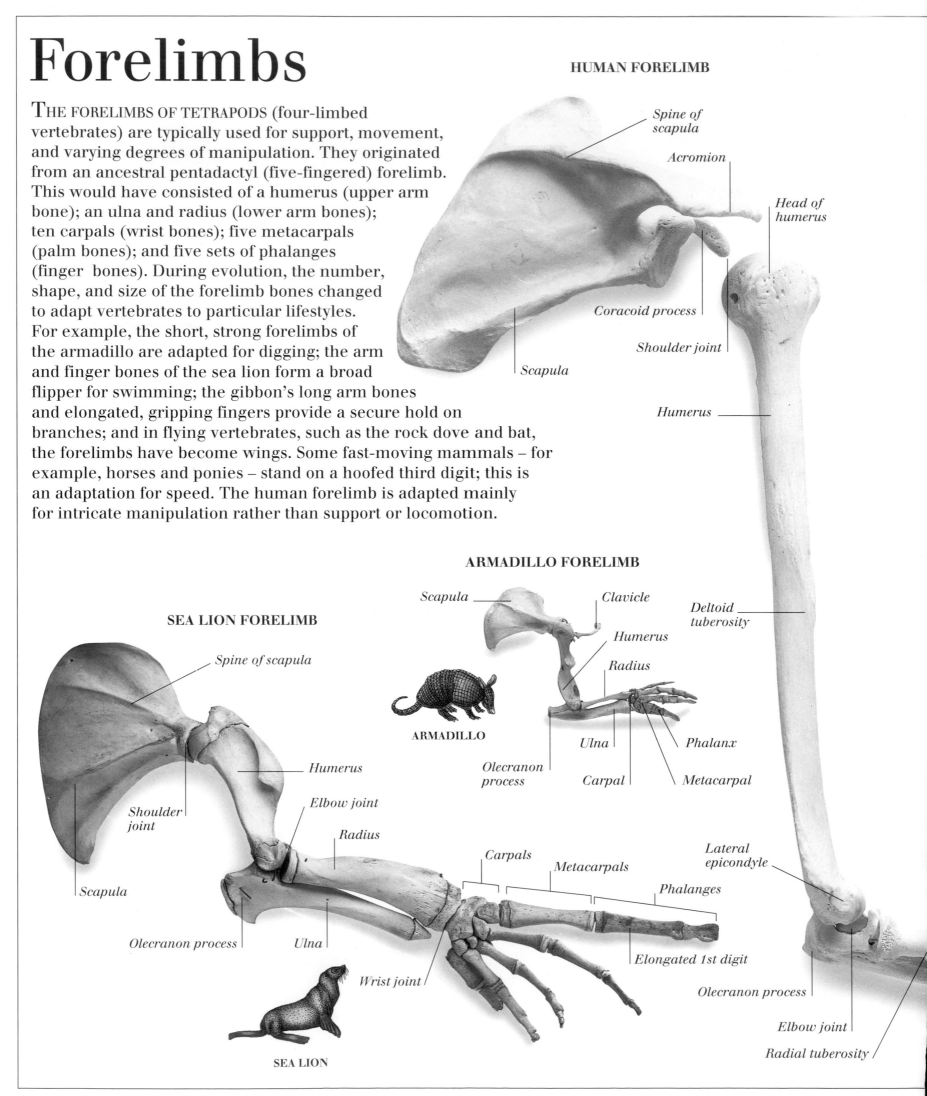

HUMAN FORELIMB

Spine of scapula
Acromion
Head of humerus
Coracoid process
Shoulder joint
Scapula
Humerus
Deltoid tuberosity
Lateral epicondyle
Olecranon process
Elbow joint
Radial tuberosity

ARMADILLO FORELIMB

Scapula
Clavicle
Humerus
Radius
ARMADILLO
Ulna
Phalanx
Olecranon process
Carpal
Metacarpal

SEA LION FORELIMB

Spine of scapula
Humerus
Shoulder joint
Elbow joint
Radius
Scapula
Olecranon process
Ulna
Wrist joint
Carpals
Metacarpals
Phalanges
Elongated 1st digit

SEA LION

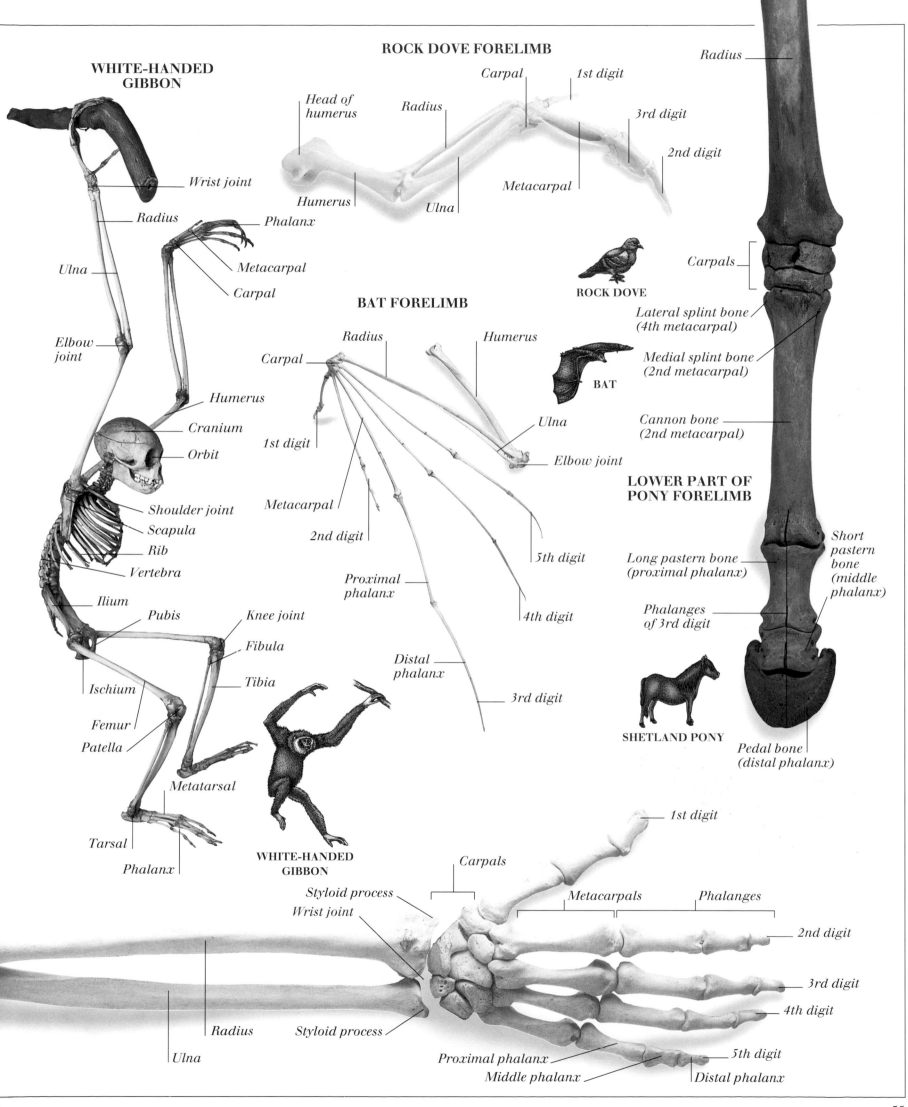

WHITE-HANDED GIBBON

Wrist joint
Radius
Phalanx
Ulna
Metacarpal
Carpal
Elbow joint
Humerus
Cranium
Orbit
Shoulder joint
Scapula
Rib
Vertebra
Ilium
Pubis
Knee joint
Ischium
Fibula
Femur
Tibia
Patella
Metatarsal
Tarsal
Phalanx

WHITE-HANDED GIBBON

ROCK DOVE FORELIMB

Head of humerus
Radius
Carpal
1st digit
3rd digit
2nd digit
Metacarpal
Humerus
Ulna

ROCK DOVE

BAT FORELIMB

Radius
Carpal
Humerus
1st digit
Metacarpal
2nd digit
Ulna
Elbow joint
Proximal phalanx
5th digit
Distal phalanx
4th digit
3rd digit

BAT

Radius

Carpals

Lateral splint bone
(4th metacarpal)
Medial splint bone
(2nd metacarpal)

Cannon bone
(2nd metacarpal)

LOWER PART OF PONY FORELIMB

Long pastern bone
(proximal phalanx)
Short pastern bone
(middle phalanx)
Phalanges
of 3rd digit
Pedal bone
(distal phalanx)

SHETLAND PONY

1st digit
Carpals
Styloid process
Metacarpals
Phalanges
Wrist joint
2nd digit
3rd digit
Radius
Styloid process
4th digit
Proximal phalanx
5th digit
Ulna
Middle phalanx
Distal phalanx

Hind limbs

THE HIND LIMBS OF TETRAPODS (four-limbed vertebrates) are more powerful than the forelimbs, and generally provide most of the locomotive force. A typical hind limb consists of a femur (upper leg bone), a tibia and fibula (lower leg bones), tarsals (ankle bones), metatarsals (middle foot bones), and phalanges (toe bones). This arrangement, like that of tetrapod forelimbs, evolved from an ancestral pentadactyl (five-fingered) limb, and is adapted to fit particular lifestyles. The seal's short hind limb and elongated foot form a flipper that propels the animal through the water. Long leg and foot bones adapt the serval for pouncing, and the wallaby for balance and a powerful hopping action. The owl's strong hind limbs can be extended to seize prey; and the gibbon uses its long toes to grip branches. The hind limb of the ox has two hoof-tipped toes and fused metatarsals to give strength. The human leg is adapted for an upright posture: the leg bones are long and strong to support body weight, and the long, broad foot provides stability.

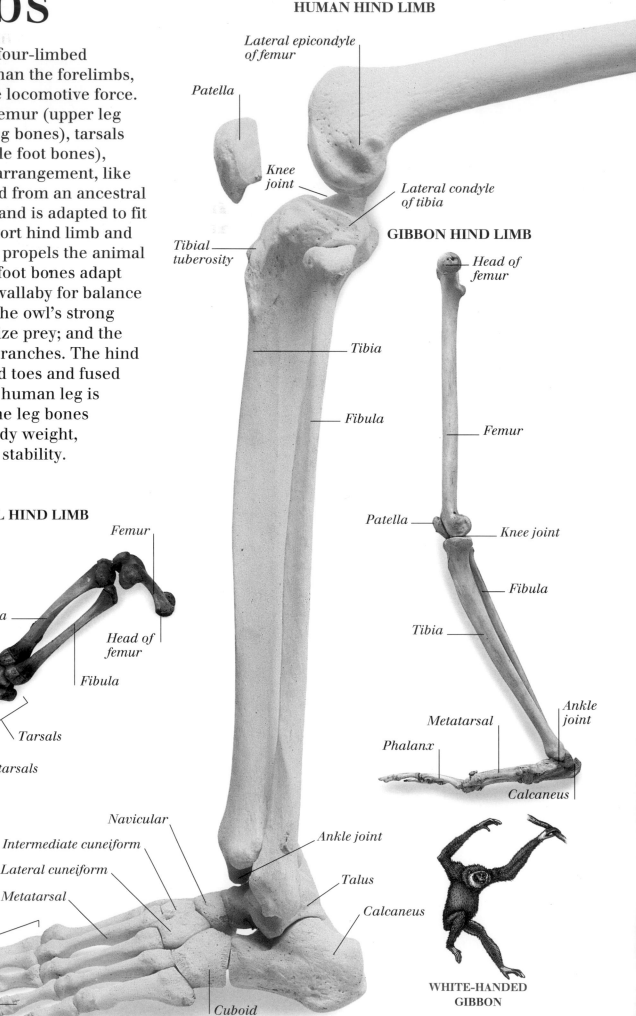

HUMAN HIND LIMB

Lateral epicondyle of femur

Patella

Knee joint

Lateral condyle of tibia

Tibial tuberosity

Tibia

Fibula

Navicular

Intermediate cuneiform

Lateral cuneiform

Metatarsal

Digit

Phalanx

Cuboid

Ankle joint

Talus

Calcaneus

GIBBON HIND LIMB

Head of femur

Femur

Patella

Knee joint

Fibula

Tibia

Metatarsal

Phalanx

Ankle joint

Calcaneus

WHITE-HANDED GIBBON

SEAL HIND LIMB

Femur

Tibia

Head of femur

Fibula

Tarsals

Metatarsals

Phalanges

SEAL

56

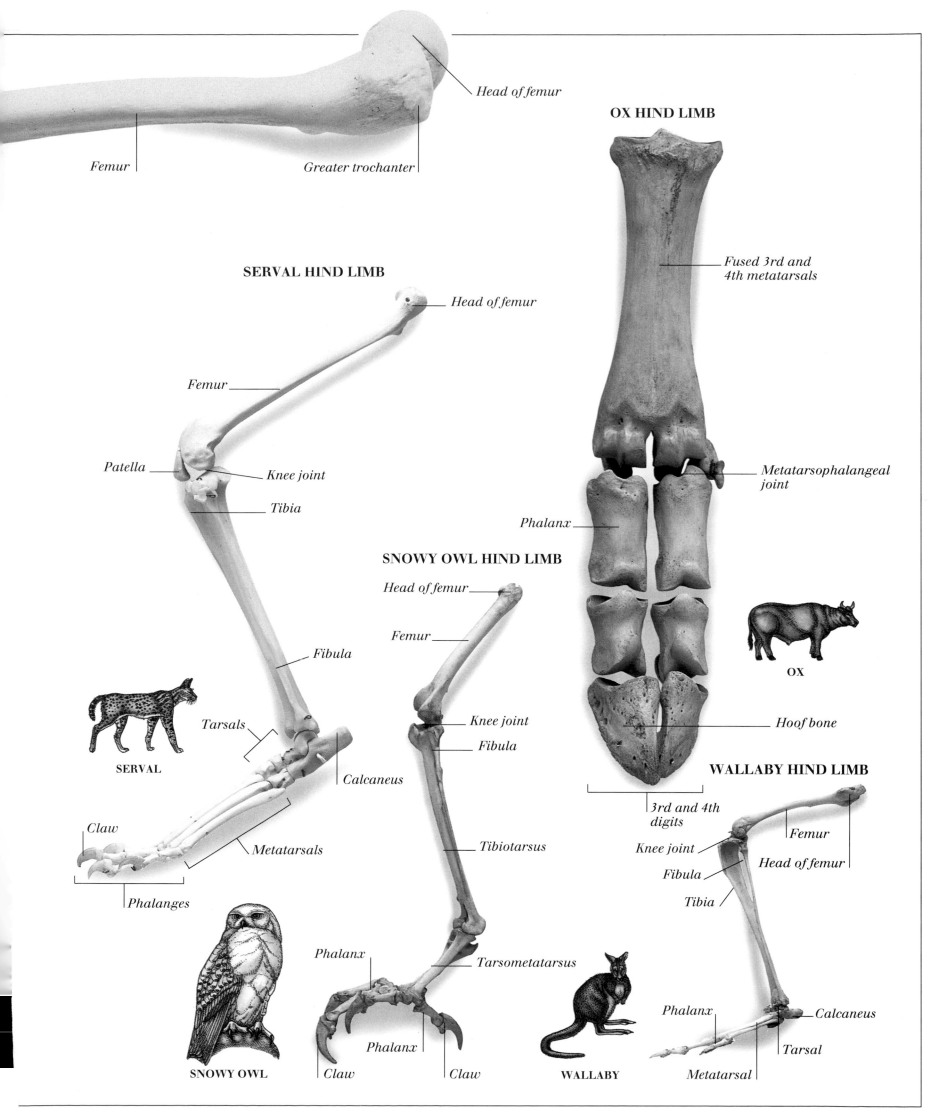

Head of femur

Femur

Greater trochanter

OX HIND LIMB

Fused 3rd and
4th metatarsals

SERVAL HIND LIMB

Head of femur

Femur

Patella

Knee joint

Tibia

Metatarsophalangeal
joint

Phalanx

SNOWY OWL HIND LIMB

Head of femur

Femur

Knee joint

Fibula

OX

Tarsals

Calcaneus

SERVAL

Hoof bone

Metatarsals

Claw

WALLABY HIND LIMB

Tibiotarsus

3rd and 4th
digits

Phalanges

Knee joint

Femur

Head of femur

Fibula

Tibia

Phalanx

Tarsometatarsus

Phalanx

Calcaneus

Claw

Phalanx

Claw

SNOWY OWL

WALLABY

Tarsal

Metatarsal

Hands and feet

THE HANDS AND FEET of most tetrapods (four-limbed vertebrates) are used for support and movement. However, the human hand is adapted for precise manipulation and grip. The skeleton of the human hand consists of phalanges (finger bones), metacarpals (palm bones), and carpals (wrist bones). The first metacarpal and trapezium bone form a highly mobile saddle joint that gives the thumb its manoeuvrability. The human foot acts as a lever to propel the body forwards, aids balance, and provides support. It consists of 26 bones: seven tarsals (ankle bones), five metatarsals (middle foot bones), and fourteen phalanges (toe bones). The hands and feet of other tetrapods are adapted to their particular lifestyles: the aye-aye's long fingers and toes grip the branches of trees; the penguin's wide foot provides balance and stability on land; and the zebra's leg rests on its third finger, increasing agility and length of stride.

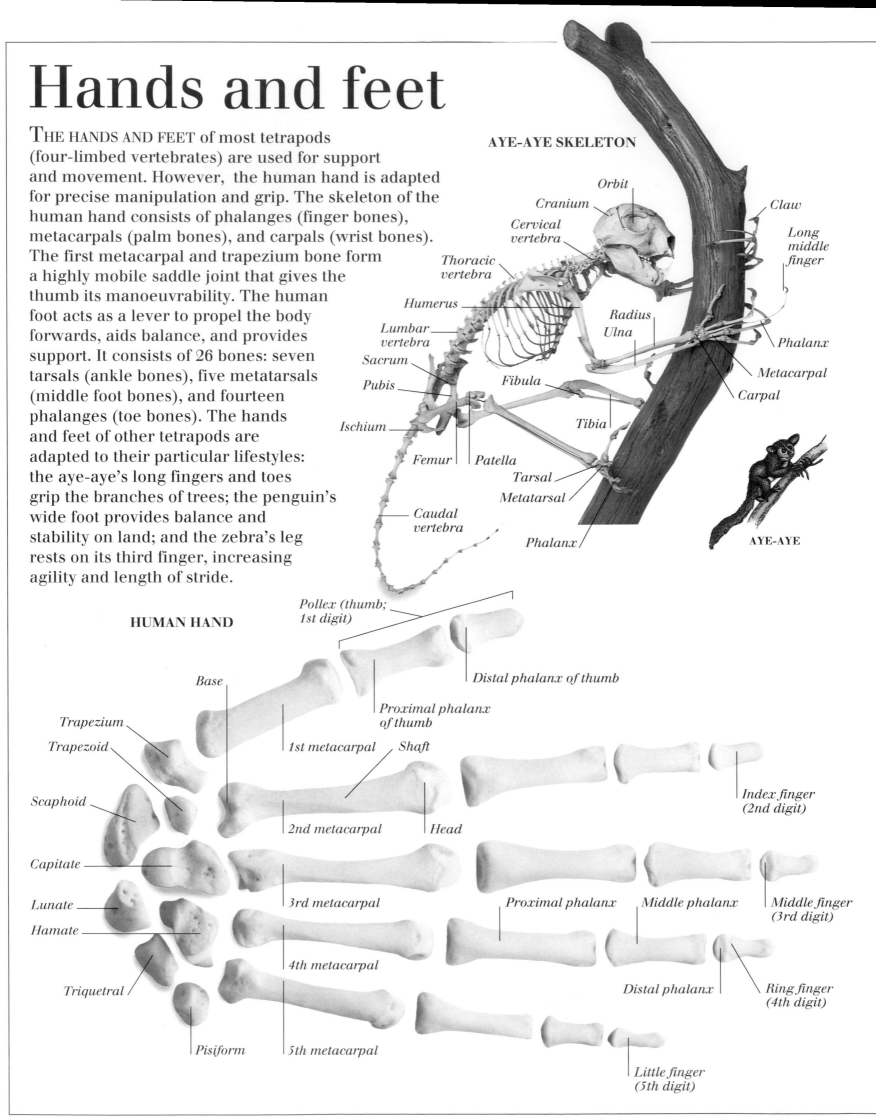

AYE-AYE SKELETON

Orbit
Cranium
Cervical vertebra
Claw
Long middle finger
Thoracic vertebra
Humerus
Radius
Ulna
Lumbar vertebra
Sacrum
Fibula
Phalanx
Pubis
Metacarpal
Carpal
Ischium
Tibia
Femur
Patella
Tarsal
Metatarsal
Caudal vertebra
Phalanx

AYE-AYE

HUMAN HAND

Pollex (thumb; 1st digit)
Base
Distal phalanx of thumb
Trapezium
Proximal phalanx of thumb
Trapezoid
1st metacarpal
Shaft
Scaphoid
Index finger (2nd digit)
2nd metacarpal
Head
Capitate
Lunate
Proximal phalanx
Middle phalanx
Middle finger (3rd digit)
Hamate
3rd metacarpal
4th metacarpal
Triquetral
Distal phalanx
Ring finger (4th digit)
Pisiform
5th metacarpal
Little finger (5th digit)

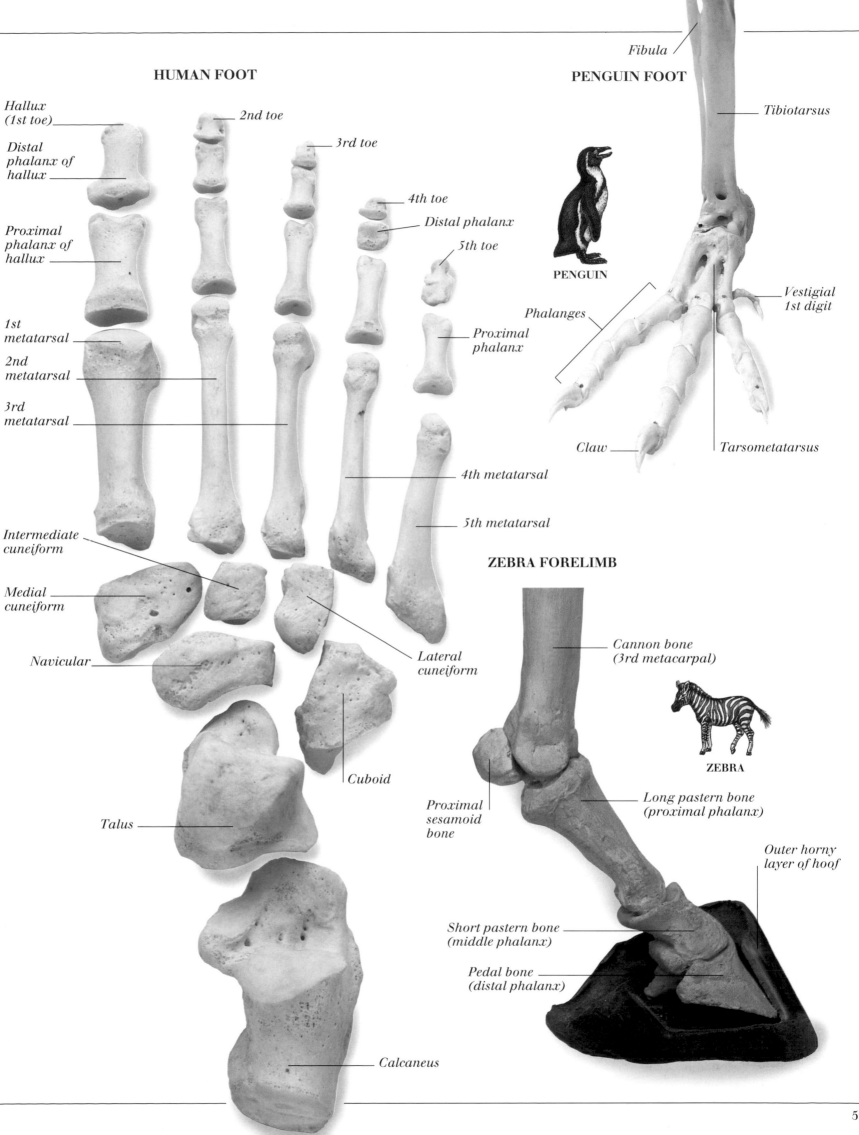

HUMAN FOOT

Hallux
(1st toe)

2nd toe

3rd toe

Distal
phalanx of
hallux

4th toe

Distal phalanx

Proximal
phalanx of
hallux

5th toe

1st
metatarsal

2nd
metatarsal

Proximal
phalanx

3rd
metatarsal

4th metatarsal

5th metatarsal

Intermediate
cuneiform

Medial
cuneiform

Navicular

Lateral
cuneiform

Cuboid

Talus

Calcaneus

PENGUIN FOOT

Fibula

Tibiotarsus

PENGUIN

Vestigial
1st digit

Phalanges

Claw

Tarsometatarsus

ZEBRA FORELIMB

Cannon bone
(3rd metacarpal)

ZEBRA

Long pastern bone
(proximal phalanx)

Outer horny
layer of hoof

Proximal
sesamoid
bone

Short pastern bone
(middle phalanx)

Pedal bone
(distal phalanx)

59

Index

Acknowledgments

Dorling Kindersley would like to thank:
Dr Chris Stringer, Dr Louise Humphrey, and
Dr Peter Andrews at the Department of
Palaeontology, The Natural History Museum,
London; Dr Gary Sawyer and Dr Allison
Andors of the American Museum of Natural
History, New York; Martin Berry, Professor of
Anatomy at Guy's Hospital, London for the
loan of the human skeleton and the male and
female pelvises; George Bridgeman at UMDS
for permission to photograph the human
skeleton and the male and female pelvises,
pp12-15, 52-53; Brandon Broll at the Science
Photo Library for editorial help and advice;
Edward Bunting and Mary Lindsay for
editorial help; Maureen Donovan for advice
on labelling the bone marrow micrograph;
Stephen Eeley, Jane Pickering, and the staff of

the Oxford University Museum for permission
to photograph exhibits; Donald Farr at King's
College, London, for editorial help and advice
on pelvises; Darren Hill and Mark Wilde for
additional design assistance.

Picture credits:
t top; *c* centre; *b* bottom; *l* left; *r* right.
The Publisher would like to thank the
following for their kind permission to
reproduce their photographs: Microscopix/
Andrew Syred 9cl, 16tr, 18tl, 40bl; Science
Photo Library/ Scott Camazine 10bl,15t;/ Eric
Grave 41b;/ Prof. P. Motta, Department of
Anatomy, University La Sapienza, Rome
front cover c,15bl,br, 40tr,cr, 41tl;/
David Scharf 41(tr)

Museum credits:
Dorling Kindersley would like to thank:
The Natural History Museum, London; The
University Museum, Oxford; The Royal Masonic
Hospital, London; The University Museum of
Zoology, Cambridge; Royal Scottish Museum,
Edinburgh; Naturmuseum Senckenburg,
Frankfurt.

Dorling Kindersley photographers:
Andy Crawford, Steve Gorton, Sarah Ashun

**Makers or owners of models shown in this
book:** John Dunlop, prepared skeletons: Dogfish
skeleton pp 22-23; Salamander skeleton
pp 24-25; Monitor Lizard skeleton pp 28-29;
Penguin skeleton p 31; Penguin foot p.59

 Somso Modelle, Coburg,
Germany: section through
buttercup root p.16; section
through young woody stem p.17;
model of skeleton p.21; hip joint with
ligaments/anatomy of hip joint p.42

Additional illustrator: Elizabeth Gray
(principal illustrators are credited
separately on p.4)

Index: Kay Wright